THE ✦ TIMES

Queen Elizabeth II

A celebration of her life and reign
1926 ~ 2022

— CONTENTS —

Editor
Bridget Harrison
Design
David Riley

Chief sub-editor
Siobhan Murphy
Picture editor
Sara Rumens

Picture research
Anna Bassett,
Russ O'Connell

With thanks to Ian Brunskill,
Odile Thomas, Nensi Kasap,
Geneva Starr, Sarah Browne,
Luke Sale, Andy Keys

COVER *Cecil Beaton's portrait of the Queen in her Coronation robes, June 1953* **LEFT** *Princess Elizabeth pictured in 1951*
OVERLEAF *The Queen photographed by Annie Leibovitz, 2007* **BACK COVER** *Pietro Annigoni's official 1955 portrait*

CECIL BEATON/CAMERA PRESS; YOUSUF KARSH/CAMERA PRESS; ANNIE LEIBOVITZ/TRUNK ARCHIVE; PIETRO ANNIGONI, GRAPHICAARTIS/BRIDGEMAN IMAGES

A Life of Service

The monarch was an anchor of stability throughout a 70-year reign in which Britain experienced immense change. The nation will forever be in her debt for her dignity, stoicism and selfless devotion to duty

THE TIMES LEADING ARTICLE FROM SEPTEMBER 9, 2022

In more than a thousand years of British history, no monarch reigned longer than Queen Elizabeth II. No other head of state today is as well travelled, as politically experienced or as astute as was the Queen. She was one of the most recognised figures in the world. For two generations of Britons, she was the embodiment of our nation, the figurehead of our democracy and the stable symbol of continuity in an increasingly turbulent and rapidly changing world. She was for most of her long life respected and admired by her many subjects, not only in Britain but around the Commonwealth that she so dearly cherished. The nation mourns her passing.

Britons born after the Queen's accession are already pensioners; four out of five alive today remember no other monarch. Those who can still look back to 1952 would see a country unrecognisable today. People still struggled through postwar austerity. Cities were black with coal soot. Schooling was dominated by the 11-plus. There were few foreign holidays, no motorways and limited television. Deference to authority, to religion and to the monarchy was axiomatic. Murderers were hanged, children were caned in schools and homosexuals were imprisoned.

In more than 3,500 acts of parliament to which the Queen gave royal assent, Britain has been utterly changed. Her subjects, too, became a different people: decades of immigration have made Britain a multi-ethnic, multicultural nation. More than two million Britons are Muslims. London, still the capital of a global empire in 1952, is now a capital of vibrant diversity, where more than a third of the population was born outside the United Kingdom. Throughout one of the greatest periods of change this country has ever known the monarchy has endured, and is as popular today as it was during the heady days of the 27-year-old Queen's Coronation in 1953. This is because the Queen knew that continuity was possible only if it embraced change. Steeped in the nation's history, traditions and ceremonies, she dedicated herself to her lifetime's role with all the seriousness, self-sacrifice and modesty that she promised in her prophetic speech on her 21st birthday: "My whole life, whether it be long or short, shall be devoted to your service" — a vow privately repeated to God beneath the canopy of her Coronation oath.

Change, though immense, was steady and almost

A studio portrait of the Queen, taken in April 1952 by Dorothy Wilding, to mark her accession

BETTMANN/GETTY IMAGES; DAVID BAILEY

imperceptible. Things once taken for granted were quietly dropped when the mores of the nation changed: early in her reign she stopped receiving debutantes at Buckingham Palace. Instead, she held tea parties in the gardens for more than 1.5 million Britons from all strata of society and allowed in thousands of tourists every summer. Men, and increasingly also women, were invited to dine with her to celebrate their achievements, not to perpetuate a class privilege. For the first 65 years of her reign she never gave a television interview; yet in 2018 she gave two, reflecting on a Coronation crown she had not seen since she wore it, and strolling among the trees of Buckingham Palace with Sir David Attenborough.

Change came sometimes at a cost. Divorce led to unhappiness in her family as much as it does in any family. At the start of her reign, the Queen had struggled when duty, public opinion and social propriety clashed with her wish for her sister Margaret's future happiness in wanting to marry a divorced man; later she was to see three of her children divorced, often in hurtful and difficult

circumstances. Her son's unhappy marriage with Diana was to take a toll on the monarchy's popularity, on her own feelings as a mother and on the stability of the throne. At a crucial moment, the Queen drew on her faith and shrewd understanding of the national mood to assert her role and pay a televised tribute to Diana after her death.

At other times she weathered the inevitable gossip, criticisms and press intrusion with stoicism, patience and discretion. In this she was aided by the wise counsel and unswerving support of Prince Philip, her beloved husband, who died last year. She made concessions: walkabouts became a royal fixture, she began to pay income tax, the royal household became more transparent and the court more egalitarian. But she did so of her own volition, responding to the public mood, of which she was a fine judge, but not visibly under duress. Rarely were her constitutional skills and role as family matriarch more sorely tested than in the handling of the scandal over Prince Andrew's links to Jeffrey Epstein and in the difficult compromise reached with her grandson, Prince Harry, and his wife, Meghan, on their wish to lay down their royal duties and live abroad. Her firm decisions on reducing their public appearances were reached with discretion and dignity.

The Queen nevertheless played a crucial role in British politics for 70 years. She took her constitutional duties extremely seriously. She read her dispatches, decorated thousands of men and women with state awards, received foreign ambassadors and outlined future legislation in her annual address from the throne at the state opening of parliament. In her last week, despite her ailing health, she accepted the resignation of Boris Johnson and appointed Liz Truss the 15th prime minister of her reign.

Her weekly audiences with her prime ministers gave her an insight, understanding of politics and historical perspective that were unrivalled. Everyone called to report to her, from Winston Churchill to Mr Johnson, with whom she continued to speak by telephone throughout the Covid-19 pandemic, was both challenged and invigorated by her gentle inquisition. Yet she perfected the art of keeping any vestige of political opinion to herself while letting her standards and her disapproval be known to others: "purring" (according to David Cameron) when told the result of the Scottish independence referendum.

At times the Queen was called on to play an almost personal political role, choosing, for instance between Rab Butler and Harold Macmillan when Anthony Eden's resignation left the Conservative party adrift. At other times she was the figurehead to signal changes in Britain's global role: visits of postwar reconciliation with Germany, a pioneering visit to post-communist Russia, the 47-year British embrace of the European Union, the many and regular visits to the United States as well as 22 to Canada, 16 to Australia and more than 100 other countries where she undertook elaborate and sometimes arduous state visits.

Perhaps more than any other public cause, the Commonwealth was one where the Queen's mind and emotions were most engaged. She began her reign at a time when much of Africa, the Caribbean and territories across Asia and the Pacific were coloured pink on the map. She travelled to many of the former colonies to celebrate their independence and to ensure, with deft authority, that links with Britain were not severed. She forged personal friendships with many African leaders, from the mercurial Kwame Nkrumah in Ghana to the exuberant Kenneth Kaunda in Zambia. These friendships gave her role as head of the Commonwealth a significance that alone kept such a disparate club together. And none was as deep, as enduring or as politically important as that with Nelson Mandela, the only foreign leader who called her just "Elizabeth" and was able to telephone her at any time of the day. Had the Queen not persisted in upholding the Commonwealth at a time when Britain seemed indifferent to its affairs, the unique 56-nation body would long ago have dissolved amid argument and differing interests. Respect for her personal engagement enabled her to pass on this role to the new King.

Indeed, it was largely thanks to her patronage that the Commonwealth was able to set up the scholarships, development funds and common professional bodies that made it both relevant and attractive to others. Countries with no historical link to Britain — Mozambique, Rwanda and Cameroon — have joined. And the one country where past bitterness severed any further association, Ireland, was where the Queen, late in her reign, undertook one of the most delicate and successful missions of reconciliation. Almost a century of bitter stereotypes on both sides of the Irish Sea were dissipated in four days of extraordinary royal diplomacy in 2011, a century after her grandfather paid the last royal visit to what was then an integral part of the United Kingdom.

Much of the Queen's stamina and moral authority came from her faith. She was, through an accident of history, the Supreme Governor of the Church of England. It was a role she embraced with utmost sincerity. Her faith was based not on intellectual curiosity or theological speculation but on the simple verities she learnt as a child, which she neither questioned nor challenged. The traditions, ceremonies and beauties of Anglican Christianity were central to her reign. She rarely missed Sunday morning service; every year she laid the wreath at the Cenotaph with reverence and feeling for the fallen; she regularly attended commemorations or celebrations in the abbeys and cathedrals of the country.

The Queen also understood that faith is not exclusive. In her words, encounters and daily deeds, she honoured the traditions of Islam, Judaism, Hinduism and the other faiths. Her Christmas broadcasts were a telling example of this. Whereas in earlier years they had been almost formulaic, offering hearty greetings and featuring her own family's Christmas decorations, in later years she seemed to speak more from her heart and her experience: encouraging compassion for the weak and downtrodden, admitting doubts and difficulties and giving a very personal account of how her faith gave her strength. Indeed, the Queen, brought up in an age of self-discipline and the stoic control of emotion, sometimes struggled to understand the

A portrait by David Bailey, taken in 2014 and released in 2017 to mark the Queen's Sapphire Jubilee

almost promiscuous parading of personal feelings among younger generations. Her own instincts of reserve and self-control were clearly at odds with the national mood at the time of Diana's death. But she did give the nation an insight into the toll that the turbulence in the lives of her children and the fire at Windsor Castle had taken when she described 1992 as her annus horribilis. And one film shot captured a rare public display of emotion as she blinked back tears at the decommissioning of the Royal Yacht Britannia.

The nation cherished the glimpses into the Queen's human responses. Never did she appear as animated as when one of her horses romped home or smile as broadly as when she was admiring a particularly fine young filly. Her wit, dry and sometimes quite pointed, was renowned, as was her talent for mimicry. And what other monarch would have agreed to take part in a James Bond spoof before the opening of the London 2012 Olympic Games? Or be filmed taking tea with Paddington Bear to open her Platinum Jubilee party?

Occasional documentaries allowed the odd look into her private quarters or caught her in unguarded exchanges. There was always a sharp mind at work, one that was not intellectual but was enriched by a huge amount of common sense and a regard for plain speaking. But the Queen well understood Walter Bagehot's famous dictum about not letting light in upon the magic. She knew she needed to show herself to her subjects. No monarch has travelled to so many parts of the country, opened so many public buildings, inaugurated so many projects or been so assiduous in visiting the bereaved, whether at Aberfan or outside Grenfell Tower. But she also knew that there needed to be limits to what the public should see. Monarchy does not work as a showbiz spectacle, whatever the efforts of the gossip columnists and paparazzi.

A constitutional monarch has the right to be consulted, the right to encourage and the right to warn, Bagehot said. The Queen well understood her rights and made full, if discreet, use of them. Indeed, in her long reign she became an expert in British constitutional law and protocol. She did not hesitate to point out any departure from military tradition or attire on parades; she knew the histories of regiments and military awards better than most commanding officers. She took meticulous care in the planning of state visits and in the level of hospitality to be offered. She would personally inspect the table arrangements before state dinners, brief herself about the preferences and interests of her guests and ensure there was no unintended breach of protocol or etiquette. Formal for her did not mean cold; it meant correct.

The monarchy became very much an institution shaped in her image. Her attention to the detail of monarchy gave her complete mastery of the royal household. Its diurnal pattern was efficient and well established, as was the calendar of events, with the regular punctuation of fixed visits, occasions and functions: Trooping the Colour, Ascot, the summer visit to Balmoral, the state opening of parliament, Remembrance Day, Sandringham and the Christmas broadcast. Yet she remained the person to whom the country turned in moments of crisis. Her broadcast in 2020 at the start of a terrible year of the coronavirus was inspirational in bolstering the nation's morale. And the image of her sitting alone in St George's Chapel in Windsor Castle during the funeral of Prince Philip when lockdown rules had forbidden contact between separate households, symbolised her stoicism and willingness to lead by example.

Britain has been profoundly influenced by her reign. The new king has had to serve a long apprenticeship. He will now have to grapple with the challenge of change, renewal and different expectations. Her shoes will be almost impossible to fill. But he would not want to do so. Her achievement was her own. The King will undoubtedly acknowledge how conscientiously she filled and moulded her role and would be wise to apply these lessons. But he will want to reign in his way, for his time. The nation will surely echo the ancient and totemic incantation that follows the acclamation of each new monarch on the death of his or her predecessor: God Save the King!

The Queen
An intimate portrait

She was a monarch with a great sense of humour, sharp opinions and a generous spirit, who could instantly put people at their ease, writes the royal biographer Sally Bedell Smith

Shortly before her 88th birthday at an otherwise routine reception at Buckingham Palace, the Queen broke into song. As she was chatting with the soprano Laura Wright, she blurted out a snippet of *Sing*, the song composed by Gary Barlow for her Diamond Jubilee.

The news sped across Twitter, not least because it contradicted the Queen's image of sombre propriety. But those who knew her best would have recalled that the Queen often entertained them by singing medleys of show tunes with her sister, Margaret, at the piano, or belted out songs while perched on a wooden box during a picnic in the Outer Hebrides.

The longest-serving monarch in British history was imbued with an unwavering sense of duty — Winston Churchill, her first prime minister, told his daughter Mary Soames he was impressed "that she always paid attention to whatever she was doing" — and her thorough training gave her an understanding of the world and the role that she would play in it. But the private Queen — Lilibet to her family — was more notable for her spontaneity. She had a great sense of humour, a gift for mimicry, sharp opinions, physical courage and a generous spirit.

From time to time we caught flashes of her mischievous streak — notably when a television audience of 900 million watched her do a surprise star turn alongside Daniel Craig's James Bond during the 2012 Olympics opening ceremony. It is said that she insisted on playing herself, after Danny Boyle, the director, first suggested Dame Helen Mirren.

In most official engagements, however, the Queen's traditionally dour demeanour masked this playful side to preserve the dignity of her role. It was an instinct honed in childhood by her formidable paternal grandmother, Queen Mary, who felt it

inappropriate for a monarch to smile in public. If the monarch was required to be serious and dutiful, Elizabeth also required herself to be prepared. On the eve of her 40th year on the throne in 1992, she said: "I have a feeling that in the end, probably, training is the answer to a great many things. You can do a lot if you are properly trained, and I hope I have been."

All her prime ministers recognised how well prepared she was. Harold Wilson felt like an "unprepared schoolboy" after his first meeting with her when he failed to answer her probing questions. He came to regard her as "a highly intelligent raconteur of the political scene".

Those who met her in confidential audiences — government officials, senior military officers, clergymen, diplomats and judges — learnt that because she stayed above politics, she could absorb information without a filter of ideology, and they relied on her to tell them what people cared about. This was a great irony because it was assumed that the lofty perch of the monarchy made it impossible to understand the everyday concerns of "commoners".

In fact over her decades of service the Queen met thousands of people a year, never once seeming impatient or bored. How she achieved this will remain part of her great mystique.

"One gets crafty after a while and learns how to save oneself," she remarked to Jacqueline Kennedy during the first lady's visit to Buckingham Palace. Years later one of the Queen's relatives asked her what she meant. "I have a knack," she said. "As soon as I stop working, I get into the car and I just switch off."

That ability to compartmentalise developed at an early age, when she would imagine herself as a pony. "When someone called her and she didn't answer right away," her cousin Lady Mary Clayton recalled, "she would then say, 'I couldn't answer you as a pony.'"

ABOVE
Princess Elizabeth enjoys a joke with her father, King George VI, in the grounds of the Royal Lodge, Windsor, in 1946

LEFT
The Queen at the Royal Windsor Horse Show in 2009

During a state visit to Washington in 1991, Benedicte Valentiner, who oversaw the president's guest quarters, watched her standing alone before half a dozen engagements. "It was as if she were looking inward, getting set," Valentiner said. "This was how she wound up her batteries. There was no chitchat, but standing absolutely still and waiting, resting in herself."

Before formal dinners the Queen sometimes relaxed through what her private secretary Sir Philip Moore called her "tiara time": she had a kit with tools that she used to decorate diamond tiaras by hooking on pearl or gemstone drops. There was also her "sharpener"; two parts Dubonnet, one part gin with an ice cube and a lemon slice, which she enjoyed before lunch most days.

Her training owed less to a standard educational curriculum than the influence of figures in her formative years. Her mother encouraged her to record her impressions in a diary each night. It became a lifelong habit, "like scrubbing your teeth", the Queen said. To help her overcome her shyness, her mother arranged role-playing exercises in which she would pretend to be the Archbishop of Canterbury or another distinguished figure.

She impressed on her the maxim that "if you find something or somebody a bore, the fault lies in you", and demonstrated how to ▸▸

walk at a measured pace as well as how to sit at a slight distance from the chair back for hours because "a lady's back should never touch the back of her chair".

Her mother instilled a deep Christian faith, reading her Bible stories and drilling her on the collects and psalms from the Book of Common Prayer. This played a vital role in how the Queen carried out her duties and coped with the ups and downs of her personal life. "She can take anything the world throws at her," Lord Carey of Clifton, the former Archbishop of Canterbury, said.

Governesses taught Elizabeth the academic basics, and Queen Mary injected rigour with the "wonderful memory training" of learning poetry by heart. Elizabeth was "obliging, eager to do her best, and happiest when she was busy", her governess Marion Crawford said.

Elizabeth's education intensified when her father took the throne and she studied the intricacies of the British constitution with Sir Henry Marten. He also taught her "to appraise both sides of a question, thus using her judgment".

Her father had a singular place in her upbringing; only he could tell her what it

ABOVE
Princess Elizabeth enjoys a game of tag with the crew of HMS Vanguard during the royal family's three-month trip to South Africa in early 1947

RIGHT
At the Royal Windsor Horse Show in 1973

was like to be monarch. She was brighter than George VI, who laboured to commit facts and figures to memory, but she watched with admiration her father's struggle to overcome his stammer and noted his diligence in jotting down ideas on a pad during meals. His "steadfastness", she later said, had been her model.

During long walks at Sandringham, Balmoral and Windsor, he gave her advice and shared his views on government and politics. She watched him reading his daily dispatch boxes, a habit she followed every day of her reign except Christmas and Easter. She even read them on weekends when she stayed with friends.

Behind that doggedness lay a light-hearted spirit. On her desk in Windsor Castle she kept one of the "Solar Queen" statuettes popularised by her Diamond Jubilee. "It drives me mad," she told her cousin Lady Elizabeth Anson with a laugh. "The sun comes out and it goes 'click, click, click' and I see myself waving to me!"

Her deadpan humour sometimes took a moment to register. In 2003 the Countess of Airlie, her lady-in-waiting, celebrated her 70th birthday at Annabel's in London, where the Queen was seated next to Robert Gascoyne-Cecil, the 7th Marquess of Salisbury. The next day the Queen had an engagement at St Albans Cathedral. As she

“

You can do a lot if you
are properly trained,
and I hope I have been

was being introduced to dignitaries by the dean of St Albans, he spotted Lord Salisbury and asked whether she knew him. "Oh yes!" she said, "Robert and I were in a nightclub last night till half past one!"

World leaders instantly relaxed in her presence. President Reagan and his wife, Nancy, arrived for breakfast on a terrace outside the Queen's bedroom at Windsor in 1982 to find American-style informality. "Lined up on a table were boxes of cereal," Nancy recalled. "I said to Prince Charles, 'What do I do?' He said, 'Just help yourself.'"

Afterwards, the Queen and Reagan took their famous ride together through the Home Park. At one point Reagan was waving so much to onlookers that she worried he might ride straight into a canal next to the Thames. Reagan described her as "charming" and observed that "she was in charge of that animal".

She could be engagingly down to earth. Her favourite activity during shooting parties was picking up the pheasants or grouse after they had been brought down. While at a shoot on a friend's estate, a wounded cock pheasant flew out of a hedge at her and knocked her down. There was

blood on her clothing from the bird and a detective standing nearby feared she had been shot. He threw himself on top of her and began giving her mouth-to-mouth resuscitation. "I consider we got to know each other rather well," she said, and hired the man for her protection force.

Even in more sedate settings, she could surprise. At a dinner given by her cousin Jean Wills, one of the guests watched as she opened her handbag to "remove a white suction cup and discreetly spit into it. The Queen then attached the cup to the underside of the table. The cup had a hook on it, and she attached her handbag to it."

The Queen's physical courage was an equally unappreciated trait. While inspecting her yearlings in a field near her stable at Polhampton, Hampshire, the six colts began galloping, rearing up and kicking out. Only the Queen and her trainer Ian Balding stayed in place. She knew that if she remained motionless, the horses would settle down. "She was completely unruffled," Balding recalled.

At the age of 55, she displayed that sangfroid to her subjects on June 13, 1981, while leading her annual birthday parade up

ABOVE
Inspecting a guard of honour outside the Canadian parliament in Ottowa during a tour in 2010

ABOVE LEFT
The Queen and the Duke of Edinburgh visiting Fiji in 1977

The Mall, riding sidesaddle on Burmese, her 19-year-old mare. As she turned towards Horse Guards Parade for the start of Trooping the Colour, six shots rang out. Her startled horse cantered forwards, and she instinctively pulled the reins with both hands. Amid the pandemonium she focused on calming Burmese, leaning down to pat the horse's neck, and proceeding at a walk.

The shots were blanks, but the Queen later revealed that in a split-second glance she had seen the man in the crowd pointing the gun and could not believe her eyes.

Perhaps her most unlikely quality was her humility. At a party in St James's Palace given by one of her cousins shortly before the wedding of Prince William and Kate Middleton, the Queen made her way happily on her own, without any attendants making introductions. It was her palace, yet she was merely another guest.

There was plenty of pomp and protocol for formal occasions, but in private — when she would "sidle into a room", as a private secretary put it, or slip into the background when someone else was being celebrated — her unaffected humility gave the Queen a special grandeur.

1920s

A PRINCESS IS BORN

The Queen's mother — the Duchess of York, as she was then — did not like White Lodge, the home in Richmond Park that King George V and Queen Mary had designated for them. It was cold and uncomfortable, with inadequate electric lighting and dubious plumbing. Understandably, the duchess decided to give birth to her first child at 17 Bruton Street, the Mayfair home of her parents, the Earl and Countess of Strathmore.

Although the new baby was not in direct line of succession — she was third in line to the throne, as her uncle, the Prince of Wales, was still expected to marry and have children — royal tradition dictated that a government minister should be in attendance: the home secretary, Sir William Joynson-Hicks, waited in the next room while the duchess went through a long, difficult labour. Afterwards, the official bulletin referred to the medical complications and "a certain line of treatment", which was the nearest anyone came to saying in public that she was delivered by caesarean section.

She was born in the early hours of Wednesday, April 21, 1926, 13 days before the start of the General Strike. It was over, however, by the time of her christening on May 29 in the private chapel of Buckingham Palace. The font Queen Victoria had used for her children's christenings was brought up from Windsor Castle, and Elizabeth was dressed

> **With her parents on a six-month official tour, Elizabeth's first birthday came and went without them**

in the Honiton lace christening robe that had been used for all Victoria's children.

The most important figure in her young life was not her mother but her nurse, Clara Knight, who was known to Elizabeth — and, later, Margaret — as Allah. When Elizabeth was just nine months old her parents went on an official tour of Australia and New Zealand that lasted six months. Her first birthday came and went without them.

Later, as Queen, Elizabeth would do the same thing, leaving Prince Charles and Princess Anne behind when she and Prince Philip went on a Commonwealth tour that lasted nearly six months. While Elizabeth's parents were away, her nanny tried to keep parental memories alive. She would show the baby a picture of her mother, and taught her to say "Mummy".

Shuffled between grandparents, she spent three months at Buckingham Palace, where she would be brought down every afternoon to have tea with the king and queen. "Here comes the bambino!" Queen Mary would cry out with delight.

For most of her childhood, home was 145 Piccadilly, a five-storey house that overlooked Green Park. Elizabeth was a neat girl: her toy ponies were always lined up in an orderly row. She even had a small red dustpan and brush, with which she was encouraged to keep her room tidy.

She saw a lot of her grandparents, and George V seemed to enjoy playing with her in a way he had not done with his own children. He would call her Lilibet, in imitation of her attempts to say her own name. The nickname stuck, and would be given another lease of life almost a century later when the Duke and Duchess of Sussex chose it as the name for their daughter.

In 1928, when Elizabeth was two and a half, Winston Churchill, then chancellor, met her while staying at Balmoral, which would become the Queen's favourite summer retreat, and was where she died on September 8, 2022. He described her in a letter as "a character", writing: "She has an air of authority and reflectiveness astonishing in an infant."

Valentine Low

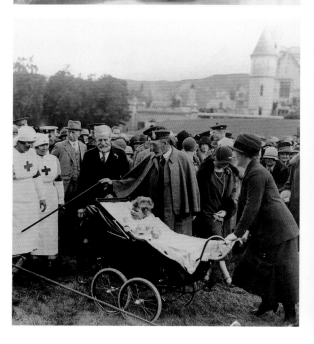

LEFT
A formal portrait of the Duke and Duchess of York — the future King George VI and Queen Elizabeth — with their first child, Princess Elizabeth

FAR LEFT, TOP
The Duchess of York with Elizabeth in May 1926, a month after her birth at 17 Bruton Street in Mayfair

FAR LEFT, CENTRE
A portrait of Elizabeth aged about two, taken in 1928. The photographer, Marcus Adams, continued to take portraits of royal children until the 1950s

FAR LEFT, BOTTOM
A picture from the Times archive shows King George V and the Duchess of York attending a fête at Balmoral with the young Elizabeth in a pram, on September 12, 1927

1930s

A NEW CALLING

The Thirties was a decade of tumultuous change for the young Princess Elizabeth. The family of three became four — "We four," as her father used to say — with the arrival of Princess Margaret on August 21, 1930. The sisters were close, but very different in temperament. While Elizabeth was dutiful, her younger sister was more extrovert: one royal writer described her as "less solemn, less conscientious and altogether less well mannered".

Marion Crawford, the princesses' young Scottish governess, provided Elizabeth's education: two and a half hours a week of poetry, literature and grammar, half an hour on the Bible, two hours each on history and arithmetic, and half an hour on geography. In the afternoon there would be dancing, drawing and music lessons. It was not a taxing regime.

Crawfie, as she was known — who later got into trouble for writing a memoir — did her best to show the princesses a life beyond the palace gates. After Elizabeth expressed a hankering to go on the Underground ("Oh dear," she said wistfully, walking past Hyde Park Corner one day, "what fun it must be to ride in those trains"), she took them for a trip on the Tube. The princesses bought their own tickets. Afterwards they visited a café, where they got shouted at by the waitress for leaving the teapot behind at the counter.

Before the Abdication of Edward VIII, Elizabeth could have looked forward to an undemanding life as one of the lesser stars in the royal firmament: one who would shine brightly when she was young, to be sure, but a figure whose importance would diminish as time passed and the king had his own family. The Abdication put paid to all that. A reluctant Duke of York became King George VI, and the family's life changed irrevocably.

Elizabeth did not need anyone to tell her that it meant she would one day accede to the throne herself. "Poor you," Margaret said.

The changes to their life were immediate, and not entirely welcome. When Crawfie told Elizabeth that they would have to move into Buckingham Palace, she stared at her in horror. "What?" she said. "You mean for ever?"

For the Coronation, Elizabeth and Margaret were dressed in ermine cloaks and coronets that had been made especially for them. Elizabeth was deeply moved by the whole occasion, and wrote an account of it. "I thought it was all very, very wonderful and I expect the Abbey did too. The arches and beams at the top were covered with a sort of haze of wonder as Papa was crowned, at least I thought so."

In 1937 it dawned on the parents of the future queen that they needed to broaden her education, and she was sent for tutorials on the British constitution with Sir Henry Marten, vice-provost of Eton. "Crawfie," she said when she saw the books lining his rooms, "do you mean to tell me he has read them all?"

In July 1939 the royal family paid a visit to the Royal Naval College, Dartmouth. Someone was needed to entertain the princesses for the afternoon and Lord Mountbatten, who was part of the royal party, came up with his nephew, Prince Philip of Greece, who was a naval cadet. Philip, who was not unknown to the royal family, showed off by jumping over a tennis net: the 13-year-old Elizabeth could not keep her eyes off him.

As George VI's official biographer, Sir John Wheeler-Bennett, wrote: "This was the man with whom Princess Elizabeth had been in love from their first meeting."

Valentine Low

> ❝ 'What?' Elizabeth said when she was told the family now had to move to Buckingham Palace. 'You mean for ever?'

ABOVE
Princess Elizabeth aged six, with Princess Margaret, riding a rocking horse at St Paul's Walden Bury, Hertfordshire, their mother's childhood home, in August 1932

LEFT
Ten-year-old Elizabeth and Margaret, five, with their mother at Royal Lodge in Windsor in the summer of 1936

RIGHT
Accompanied by the chairman of the Richmond Horse Show, Princess Elizabeth strokes one of the prize-winning ponies during a visit in June 1934. Her grandfather George V encouraged her love of horses from a young age »

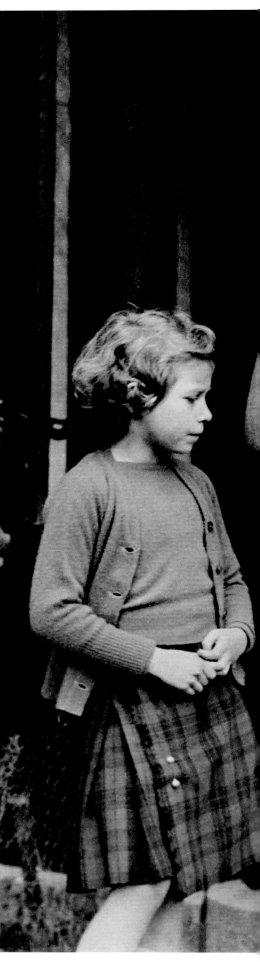

TOP
In March 1933, a few weeks before she turned seven, Princess Elizabeth was photographed on an early spring stroll with two nannies through Hyde Park. Princess Margaret is in the pram

ABOVE
Princess Elizabeth and her mother attend the Lyceum Theatre in London, which was famous for its pantomimes, to see a performance of Dick Whittington on February 6, 1935

BETTMANN, POPPERFOTO/
GETTY IMAGES, AP

RIGHT
The princesses in 1935 with their father, left, and uncle, who would become King Edward VIII the following year on the death of George V, only to abdicate and pass the crown to his brother »

ABOVE
The situation in Europe was growing more tense by the day, but the princesses were still allowed the occasional treat, such as this day out at London Zoo in May 1939

LEFT
The young princesses attend an inspection of the Royal Company of Archers at the Palace of Holyroodhouse, Edinburgh, with their mother and their father, far right, who had been crowned King George VI two months earlier, in May 1937

ABOVE
Princess Elizabeth at a concert for children to celebrate her father's Coronation, in Westminster, April 1937

1940s

WAR AND ROMANCE

After the war broke out, London was deemed no longer safe for the two princesses, and they moved to Windsor: first to Royal Lodge, then to the castle itself. Although Elizabeth and Margaret effectively disappeared from public view, they made their own contribution to the war effort with a radio broadcast aimed at children in October 1940, during the height of the Blitz. The 14-year-old Elizabeth did all the talking, but Margaret joined her in wishing their listeners good night. Some considered it mawkish, but the singer and actress Joyce Grenfell wrote to her mother: "It was one of the loveliest things I've ever heard."

As she grew older, Elizabeth begged her father to let her play a more active role in the war. Eventually he capitulated, and in March 1945 she joined the Auxiliary Territorial Service, learning how to drive and repair a truck. Her ATS uniform came into good use on VE Day when, after no fewer than six appearances with her parents on the balcony of Buckingham Palace, she pulled her cap low down over her eyes and went out with Margaret and a group of friends to join the crowds on the street. She joined the throng outside the palace shouting: "We want the king! We want the king!" It was, she said later, "one of the most memorable nights of my life".

Meanwhile, she never forgot the handsome young naval cadet she had met just before the war. Philip would write to her, and when he was on leave he would come and stay at Windsor Castle. Once, when Elizabeth learnt he was coming to see one of the pantomimes that she and Margaret would put on at Christmas, she said to her governess: "Who do you think is coming to see us act, Crawfie?"

By 1946 there was little doubt about their relationship. People got so used to seeing Philip around that on one of Elizabeth's public engagements the crowd shouted: "Where's Philip?"

The king wanted her to wait, however, and Elizabeth came to an agreement with her father: she would accompany her parents on a tour of South Africa, and if she still wanted to marry Philip on her return, he would give his consent.

While she was there she made a radio broadcast in Cape Town on her 21st birthday, in which she dedicated herself to the Empire. It would remain one of the most famous speeches of her life. "I declare before you all that my whole life, whether it be long or short, shall be devoted to your service and the service of our great imperial family to which we all belong."

She and Philip married at Westminster Abbey on November 20, 1947. With rationing still in force, and the country only just out of a fuel crisis, it was a much needed moment of national celebration. Elizabeth's wedding dress, which was designed by Norman Hartnell, was made possible thanks to a special allowance of 200 clothing coupons — the usual wartime allowance for a family of four was 48 coupons a year.

It was not quite, however, the great joining of two families that a wedding of this nature normally implies. Philip's sisters, who all married Germans, were not invited. But a host of crowned heads — and former crowned heads — appeared from all over Europe and beyond, including the kings of Norway, Romania and Iraq, and the king and queen of Denmark. As Princess Margaret put it: "People who had been starving in little garrets all over Europe suddenly reappeared."
Valentine Low

> ❝
> Princess Elizabeth never forgot the handsome young naval cadet she had met just before the war

Princess Elizabeth during her time in the Auxiliary Territorial Service. She joined in March 1945 as a 2nd subaltern and trained as a truck driver and mechanic »

ABOVE
*In February 1943
the princesses
released a carrier
pigeon with a
message for Lady
Baden-Powell,
the Chief Guide,
to mark her late
husband's birthday*

BELOW
*Accompanied by
her younger sister,
Elizabeth makes
her first broadcast
at the age of 14,
in October 1940.
"When peace
comes," she
told the young* *people of the
Commonwealth,
"remember it
will be for us, the
children of today,
to make the world
of tomorrow
a better and
happier place"*

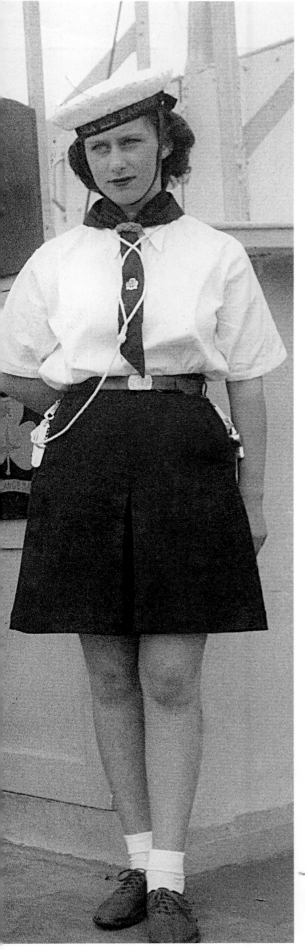

LEFT
In 1944 the princesses were back in Dartmouth, where Elizabeth had first met Philip in 1939, pictured here aboard a converted motor torpedo boat used by local Sea Rangers

RIGHT
In the spring of 1942, Princess Elizabeth and Princess Margaret were pictured at Royal Lodge, Windsor, with their Lhasa apso dog

BELOW
The 15-year-old Princess Elizabeth — who had joined the Girl Guides as an 11-year-old — learns how to tie a knot at Frogmore, Windsor, April 1942 »

ABOVE
On VE Day, May 8, 1945, as the huge crowds outside Buckingham Palace chanted, "We want the King", the royal family and the prime minister Winston Churchill appeared on the balcony. Princess Elizabeth is wearing her khaki uniform of the Auxiliary Territorial Service

LEFT
A year earlier amid D-Day preparations, Princess Elizabeth inspects an honour guard during a royal visit to the 5th Guards Armoured Brigade at Hove, East Sussex, May 1944

ABOVE
Their father had been king for nearly a decade when this portrait of the family was taken in the summer of 1946 in the grounds of Royal Lodge, Windsor

LEFT
On her 21st birthday, in 1947, Princess Elizabeth broadcasts a speech to the people of the Commonwealth from Cape Town, South Africa: "I declare before you all that my whole life, whether it be long or short, shall be devoted to your service"

RIGHT
Princess Elizabeth and Princess Margaret attend a cricket match at Eton, June 1947 »

King George VI, Margaret and Elizabeth and Prince Philip attend the wedding of Lady Patricia Mountbatten, in October 1946. This was the first time Elizabeth had been seen publicly with Prince Philip

LEFT
Princess Elizabeth and Prince Philip greet guests at a Buckingham Palace garden party in July 1947, the day after their engagement was announced

RIGHT
Three weeks before their wedding in November 1947, Elizabeth and Philip visited Clydebank in Scotland, where they were given a Singer sewing machine made in the town

Princess Elizabeth and Prince Philip at Buckingham Palace after the announcement of their engagement on July 9, 1947 »

Princess Elizabeth and the Duke of Edinburgh pictured at Buckingham Palace on their wedding day, November 20, 1947. The party includes the king and queen (front row, third and second from right), Princess Margaret (back row, fourth from right), the duke's best man, David Mountbatten, the 3rd Marquess of Milford Haven, Queen Mary, Elizabeth's grandmother, and Princess Alice, Philip's mother (front row, first and second from left)

Love, loyalty and a lasting partnership

The Queen's marriage to Prince Philip underpinned the most successful monarchy
that the United Kingdom has known, the royal biographer Sally Bedell Smith writes

Several days before the Queen and the Duke of Edinburgh marked their 70th wedding anniversary with a formal dinner at Windsor Castle in November 2017, they attended a considerably smaller private gathering in London. At the age of 96, Prince Philip had officially retired from public life in August and was dividing his time between Windsor Castle and Wood Farm at the Queen's Sandringham estate in Norfolk. He hadn't been expected at the dinner but decided at the last minute to attend.

The guest list was grand, including King Harald V of Norway and Queen Sonja, King Willem-Alexander of the Netherlands and Queen Máxima, but the atmosphere was cosy and light-hearted. At the end of the dinner, the Queen got into her limousine, bound for Buckingham Palace, and the duke climbed into his car, headed for Windsor Castle. Suddenly a window in Philip's car rolled down and he shouted to his wife: "GOODBYE!" She rolled down her window and responded with equal vigour: "GOODBYE!"

Such moments are seldom glimpsed by those outside the Queen and the duke's circle. The enduring public image was typified during her Diamond Jubilee weekend in June 2012, when they stood on the deck of the royal barge for nearly four hours in the rain. Then aged 86 and 90, braving chill and blustery winds, they showed fortitude as well as gratitude to the 1.2 million people who had gathered along the banks of the Thames.

It was everything that symbolised the royal couple. They were tough, stoic, duty-bound, a team. A beacon of continuity throughout decades of change, they set an example and solidified the traditions that help to bind the nation. Their mutual devotion radiated a "sense of unqualified

> " If the Queen was constant and calm, Philip was a spritz of vinegar

commitment that has been so characteristic of every aspect of this reign", the Archbishop of Canterbury, Rowan Williams, said when they celebrated their 60th wedding anniversary in 2007.

In the years after Prince Philip's retirement, the Queen respected his wish to live amid the simplicity and informality of Wood Farm, where the staff dispensed with the traditional livery required in the Queen's residences. He had friends over to shoot rabbits, visited neighbours for lunch, and relished the migration of birds on the marshes. However, when he needed hip replacement surgery in early April 2018, she insisted he recuperate at Windsor Castle.

Determined to attend the wedding of Prince Harry without using a stick, Philip regained his mobility in the long castle corridors. "There's Philip careering around on crutches!" the Queen exclaimed to a friend on the telephone one day. "Quite far behind him is the nurse with her arms outstretched to catch him if he falls. But he's in the wrong place!" On Harry and Meghan's wedding day in May, Philip walked unaided.

The Queen visited her husband quietly at Wood Farm and went to some lengths to ensure he had enough stimulation for his bright and active mind as he coped with diminishing vision and hearing. He didn't like doing puzzles or playing Patience, but he enjoyed reading, so she had a device installed that would project a book on to a screen. When he insisted on driving his horse-drawn carriages round the Sandringham estate — often with a pretty neighbour he had tutored in the sport — the Queen didn't object. It kept him physically active, and offered an escape valve for the independent spirit that had appealed to her so many decades earlier.

During the spring of 2020 that arrangement was upended by the Covid-19 pandemic and the couple moved to Windsor Castle to self-isolate with a small "bubble" of staff. With all face-to-face royal duties suspended and contact with other family members confined to video calls, the isolation gave them a rare opportunity to spend quality time together, dining with each other most evenings. It was here they spent her 94th birthday in April and his 99th in June, for which they released a photograph standing together in the sun in the quadrangle at Windsor Castle.

If the Queen was constant and calm, Philip was a spritz of vinegar with his irreverent and, at times, caustic comments. However, the duke always said "supporting the Queen" was his primary purpose as her consort. Their marriage arguably held the royal family together through the divorces of three of their four children, and the harrowing week after the death of Diana, Princess of Wales in 1997. For Britain and the Commonwealth, their remarkable partnership created the most successful and beloved monarchy in history.

Princess Elizabeth could have chosen from what her friend Lady Anne Glenconner called "a whole battalion of

On their trips at home and abroad they perfected a choreography of turns and cues that appeared effortless. He watched her intently during walkabouts to see if she required assistance. He would often spot people who couldn't see her — children in particular — and guide them to a better vantage point. When the Queen needed a boost, he was there with a humorous aside: "Don't look so sad, sausage."

While they were not physically demonstrative, they had a deep connection that intensified after the deaths of her mother and sister in 2002, when he became "her emotional touchstone", in the view of one of her senior advisers. On the eve of her Diamond Jubilee, the adviser noticed that "she still lights up when he walks into the room. She becomes softer, lighter and happier." During his carriage-driving competitions, she would watch him do the obstacles, then jump into her Land Rover to drive to the next set of challenges.

Yet they were not, according to their cousin Lady Pamela Hicks, "sweet old Darby and Joan by any means. They were both very strong characters." The Queen went to unusual lengths to avoid confrontations with her prickly husband. Tony Parnell, for 30 years the foreman of her home at Sandringham, recalled a time when Philip's dressing room badly needed repainting. "On Her Majesty's instruction," he said, "we had to match the dirty paintwork so he wouldn't know."

The most poignant moment of the Diamond Jubilee weekend occurred when Philip became ill with a bladder infection after the long Thames River Pageant on the Sunday. The Queen's walk down the aisle of St Paul's Cathedral that Tuesday was a throat-catching moment — the first time she had appeared at a key ceremonial event without Philip at her side.

He was again at her side, however, for the final year of his life, an unintended silver lining of the pandemic. It seemed somehow fitting that the couple could enjoy a sunset honeymoon at Windsor Castle, where Philip had first courted Lilibet during the Second World War. When he fell ill in early 2021 and was taken to hospital for a month, he was determined to return to his own bed in the castle. The Queen was always nearby during his last three weeks as she ensured that he was comfortable and could eat and sleep whenever he wished. The end came gently, with his wife of 73 years a comforting presence.

Among her many happy memories was the 66th wedding anniversary they celebrated in typically low-key fashion at the home of the Queen's cousin, Lady Elizabeth Anson. For the dinner, she used solar-powered Queen statuettes to hold the place cards for the guests, marking the Queen's seat with a toy bobble-head corgi. Surrounded by their oldest friends and extended family, the royal couple, aged 87 and 92, still laughed like newlyweds.

lively young men", English aristocrats with vast wealth. However, at the age of 13 she fell in love when she spent an afternoon with 18-year-old Prince Philip of Greece and Denmark. He was a naval officer in training and a second cousin once removed, descended from Queen Victoria and Prince Albert. He had little money, but was handsome, confident, intelligent and energetic.

Over the years Elizabeth came to view Philip as a man of ideas and appealing complexity who would be neither easy nor boring, but would share her commitment to duty and service. Despite a protective shell formed during a rootless childhood, "Philip had a capacity for love which was waiting to be unlocked", said their mutual cousin, Patricia Mountbatten. Elizabeth "would not have been a difficult person to love", she said. "She was beautiful, amusing and gay." Her curly brown hair framed her porcelain complexion, with cheeks that the photographer Cecil Beaton described as "sugar-pink", vivid blue eyes, a dazzling smile and an infectious laugh.

They were married on November 20, 1947, and spent their honeymoon at Balmoral in Scotland. They had only a few years before she acceded to the throne at

ABOVE
The Queen and Prince Philip marked their diamond wedding anniversary in 2007 by revisiting Broadlands in Hampshire, where they spent their wedding night

LEFT
On honeymoon in November 1947 at Broadlands, the home of Prince Philip's uncle Lord Mountbatten

the age of 25. Their time in Malta from 1949 to 1951, when Philip was posted there with the Royal Navy, was the closest the princess came to an ordinary existence — socialising with other officers' wives, going to the hair salon, even carrying her own cash, although shopkeepers noted "she was slow in handling money".

It was Philip who broke the news to his wife on February 6, 1952, that her father had died, aged 56, and that she was Queen. At first, Philip was viewed with suspicion by her old-style courtiers. He was excluded from the substance of the Queen's official life, with no access to state papers. However, he carved out a role as a patron of nearly 800 charities, even as his wife came to rely on him for advice when making tough decisions.

If her advisers brought a question to her on a matter outside her head of state role, she asked them first to find out what Philip thought. She looked at the big picture and asked for other options; Philip drilled down and got to the heart of an issue — what one of her advisers called "a defence staff rigour". Early on, Philip saw the potential of television; he encouraged the Queen to use it and tutored her on how to read from an Autocue for her first televised speech in 1957.

1950s

THE KING IS DEAD, LONG LIVE THE QUEEN

The decline of George VI's health meant that Elizabeth and Philip began to take on an increasing amount of her father's workload. After the king had an operation to remove his left lung, the couple replaced her parents on a five-week tour of Canada in autumn 1951, leaving Charles and his new sister, Anne, at home. The tour included a visit to Washington, where President Truman said: "When I was a little boy I read about a fairy princess, and there she is."

There was another tour the next year, due to take in Ceylon, Australia and New Zealand. In early 1952, when Elizabeth and Philip left for the four-month trip, the king and queen came to see them off at the airport. Photographs show the king looking gaunt and strained.

The trip began with a short holiday in Kenya, where the couple stayed for a night at the Treetops Hotel. With its viewing platform by a lake, it was an ideal place to watch big game.

In the early hours of February 6, George VI died in his sleep at Sandringham of a coronary thrombosis. He was 56 years old. The news took several hours to reach Elizabeth, of whom it was famously said that she climbed a tree a princess and descended it a queen. Not that she realised it at the time; the first person in their party to hear the news was her private secretary Martin Charteris, who picked it up from a journalist at a nearby hotel. He told Philip's equerry, Michael Parker, who in turn

> ## Asked what she was going to call herself as queen, she replied, 'My own name, of course — what else?'

told Philip. He took Elizabeth — still only 25 — into the garden of Sagana Lodge, their main base in Kenya, and they walked as he broke the news to her. Pamela Hicks, one of the royal party, recalled: "One just thought, this poor girl who really adored her father. They were very close. And I think I gave her a hug and said how sorry I was. And then suddenly, I thought, my God, but she's Queen!"

Before they returned, Charteris asked her what she was going to call herself. "My own name, of course — what else?" Back in London, when she was formally proclaimed Queen at St James's Palace, she told the Privy Council: "My heart is too full for me to say more to you today than that I shall always work as my father did."

Within days there was a bitter dispute over the question of the family's name. Lord Mountbatten, Philip's uncle, had made the mistake of boasting that the "House of Mountbatten now reigned". This promptly ran into opposition from Queen Mary, the Queen Mother and the prime minister, Winston Churchill, who was no fan of Mountbatten. The Queen, torn between loyalty to her husband and the royal family, opted for the latter: the House of Windsor it remained. Philip complained that his name was taken away. "I'm nothing but a bloody amoeba," he said.

The Coronation did not take place until June 2 the following year. It was the first time it was televised, an innovation initially resisted by the Palace. It was Britain's last great imperial hoorah, a massive celebration that saw huge crowds line the streets and more than 8,000 people crammed into Westminster Abbey. Afterwards, at Buckingham Palace, the Queen sat down with her crown off while four-year-old Prince Charles played hide-and-seek under the Queen Mother's robes.

Five months later the couple departed on a Commonwealth tour. "Let us recognise how immeasurable a responsibility rests upon the shoulders of our young Queen," Lord Salisbury told the House of Lords, "for on the personal loyalties of her peoples the whole future of a free world may depend."
Valentine Low

FAR LEFT
Dressed as a peeress of the realm and wearing the Diamond Diadem, the Queen makes her way to Westminster Abbey for her Coronation. Years later the royal commentator Alastair Bruce asked her what it was like to travel in the gold state coach. "Horrible!" she replied. "It's not meant for travelling in at all. It's only sprung on leather... not very comfortable"

LEFT, TOP
Princess Elizabeth was visiting the Treetops safari lodge in Kenya when her father died and she acceded to the throne

LEFT, BOTTOM
The Queen arrives at Heathrow from Kenya after the death of her father. There to meet her was Winston Churchill, the prime minister (far right), with Clement Attlee, leader of the opposition, on his left. Anthony Eden, the deputy prime minister, and Lord Woolton, who presided over meetings of the privy council, were also in attendance »

ABOVE
The gold state coach and Coronation procession passes through a crowded Piccadilly Circus

RIGHT
The moment the Archbishop of Canterbury places the St Edward's crown on the Queen's head at the Coronation at Westminster Abbey, June 2, 1953. This was the only time the Queen wore this crown, which is set with rubies, sapphires, amethysts and topazes, and weighs 5lb. It has been used for coronations since 1661. There were 8,251 guests at the ceremony, including representatives from 129 nations and territories

LEFT
Wearing the imperial state crown, the new Queen returns to Buckingham Palace with Prince Philip to greet the crowds from the balcony »

ABOVE
Frank Sinatra is presented to the Queen at the premiere of Me and the Colonel, a comedy starring Danny Kaye, at the Odeon in Leicester Square, London, in October 1958

ABOVE
The Canadian photographer Donald McKague took a series of portraits of the Queen in December 1958. This, a rare colour picture, is among the formal ones

ABOVE
The Queen and Prince Philip visit Hamilton, Bermuda, in 1953 during a six-month tour of Commonwealth countries that included Jamaica, the Pacific Islands, New Zealand and Australia

ABOVE
On the bridge of the Gothic, passing through the Panama Canal in 1953. Next stops on the tour were Fiji and Tonga in the Pacific

LEFT
The big communications innovations of her reign may still have been decades away in 1958, when this was taken, but the Queen is nonetheless marking a significant advance here, making the first trunk call on the Bristol telephone exchange. The recipient? The lord provost of Edinburgh

RIGHT
Inspecting the men of the newly renamed Queen's Own Nigeria Regiment at Kaduna airport, Nigeria, on her 1956 tour »

BETTMANN, REG SPELLER, FOX PHOTOS/HULTON ARCHIVE/GETTY IMAGES; DONALD MCKAGUE/CAMERA PRESS; TIMES NEWSPAPERS LTD; KEYSTONE

An expert in horse racing and breeding, the Queen leads her first Oaks winner at Epsom — a filly named Carrozza, ridden by Lester Piggott. The prize money of £16,101 enabled the Queen to become the leading owner in Britain in 1957

Princess Elizabeth and two-year-old Prince Charles pose for Cecil Beaton in 1950 while playing in the grounds of Clarence House, London, where the princess and her young family had lived since her marriage three years earlier »

ABOVE
*Princess Anne's christening in October 1950. She wears the
Honiton lace robe worn by more than 60 British royals*

ABOVE
*The Queen at Balmoral in September 1952, with Prince Charles,
three, and Princess Anne, who had turned two the month before*

The royal family at the Badminton Horse Trials in 1952: seated centrally, from left, the Queen Mother, Princess Margaret and the Queen, who is pictured with a cine camera. She was given her first one as a young girl and became a proficient and prolific chronicler of family life

1960s

CHANGING TIMES
FOR A YOUNG FAMILY

On February 19, 1960, the Queen gave birth to her third child, Andrew. Although it had been ten years since Anne was born, Andrew's arrival was no accident: the Queen told her private secretary, Martin Charteris, that she and Philip had been trying for another child for some time.

While the Queen had been a somewhat distant parent with Charles and Anne — for all that she loved them both, and spent time with them when she could, affairs of state usually took precedence — by the time Andrew was born, followed four years later by Edward, she took time off to be more closely involved with their upbringing. By then she seemed to be relaxed around her children. "She was a less natural mother with Charles and Anne," one insider suggested, "whereas she was much more the besotted parent with Andrew and Edward."

Her pregnancy with Andrew forced her to cancel a visit to Ghana, which had recently become the first of Britain's tropical African colonies to achieve independence. Instead she had taken the unusual step of inviting Ghana's leader, Kwame Nkrumah, to Balmoral instead.

The rescheduled visit to Ghana took place in November 1961, eight months after her first state visit to India. There was pressure for it to be cancelled, both because of the threat of violence — bombs had exploded in Accra the week before — and opposition to Nkrumah's authoritarianism. But against a backdrop of growing communist influence in Africa, the Queen was determined to go ahead, believing that the visit would play an important role in holding the Commonwealth together.

It was a great success, even if the Queen's turn around the dancefloor with Nkrumah prompted a South African paper to complain about "the honoured head of the once mighty British Empire dancing with black natives of pagan Africa". The Ghanaian press hailed her as "the greatest socialist monarch in the world".

In the late Sixties the Queen took a decision that continues to divide opinion to this day: she co-operated with the creation of a documentary, *Royal Family*. While the Queen was initially sceptical — she was not going to play up for the cameras — her press secretary, William Heseltine, played an important role in winning her around.

The film, made by the BBC film-maker Richard Cawston, portrays a year in the life of the royal family. There is footage of the Queen at a Buckingham Palace garden party, of Charles bicycling through Cambridge as an undergraduate, of Philip flying a plane. One of the more famous sequences shows the royal family enjoying a picnic at Balmoral, with Philip in charge of the barbecue.

According to Heseltine, Philip found it harder than the Queen to get used to the presence of the camera crew. "He was, as is sometimes his wont, a little impatient with them when they appeared, as he thought, rather too close for comfort."

Royal Family was a huge success. It was shown twice in June 1969, first on the BBC and then on ITV, and was seen by more than two thirds of the population. But was it a good idea?

It allowed the royals to be seen as an ordinary family and, argued many, did the monarchy significant good. But it also blurred the line between the public and the private, and can be seen as opening the doors for an ever more intrusive media. That is a theory that is rejected by Heseltine: the media was well on its way to becoming a far less respectful institution than it once was, he said. But, as more than one commentator has pointed out, after its initial transmissions, *Royal Family* has not been seen in full since.
Valentine Low

> **"**
> **The documentary Royal Family was a huge success, seen by more than two thirds of the population**

The Queen and Prince Philip visit the Taj Mahal during a six-week tour of India, Pakistan and Nepal in 1961 ❯❯

The Queen in 1964, stroking her favourite horse, Betsy, a brown-black mare she rode through the 1960s. This was taken at Sandringham

ABOVE
The Queen, pictured with one of her gundogs, Wren, at the 1967 Open Stake Retriever Trials at Balmoral, took great pleasure in country pursuits

ABOVE
John F Kennedy, in his first few months as US president, and the first lady Jackie Kennedy were invited to Buckingham Palace for a state dinner in June 1961. The president would later write to Her Majesty: "We shall always cherish the memory of that delightful evening"

ABOVE
Visiting the Liberation Monument in Addis Ababa during a state visit to Ethiopia in February 1965

ABOVE
The Queen visited the Isle of Wight in 1965, a place much loved by her great-great-grandmother, Queen Victoria, who took annual holidays there »

LEFT
Captain Bobby Moore receives
the Jules Rimet trophy from
the Queen after England's
4-2 World Cup final win over
West Germany at Wembley
on July 30, 1966. This moment,
handing Moore the cup,
was one the Queen reflected
on more than five decades
later — "I saw what it meant
to the players, management
and support staff" — in a
written message to the present
manager, Gareth Southgate,
and his England side the day
before their Euro 2020 final
against Italy »

ABOVE
The Queen and Prince Andrew at the Braemar Gathering, Aberdeenshire, in 1968. These annual Highland games take place less than ten miles from Balmoral and include traditional contests such as caber tossing

LEFT
Prince Charles giving his youngest brother, five-year-old Edward, a ride in a go-kart in April 1969

RIGHT
The Queen and Prince Philip visiting Aberfan, south Wales, on October 29, 1966, eight days after the mining disaster that killed 116 children and 28 adults when an avalanche of slurry engulfed Pantglas Junior School and a neighbouring row of houses. The Queen later described her delay in visiting the village following the tragedy as the biggest regret of her reign »

ABOVE AND RIGHT
The documentary Royal Family, which was broadcast in June 1969, was conceived to show the day-to-day life of the Queen. From top: the family at Sandringham with a model of Captain Cook's ship, the Endeavour; decorating a Christmas tree; lunch with Charles and Anne, and, right, together at Windsor »

ROLLS PRESS, POPPERFOTO, BETTMANN, HULTON ARCHIVE/GETTY IMAGES

ABOVE
*The Queen and Prince Philip watching the competitors
at the Badminton Horse Trials in Gloucestershire, 1968*

ABOVE
*Harold Wilson — long considered to be one of the Queen's favourite
prime ministers — at Buckingham Palace in June 1969*

On board one of the Queen's Flight's Andovers after a trip to Yorkshire, a scene also captured in the 1969 documentary Royal Family »

RIGHT
Originally planned for 1959, but cancelled when she became pregnant for the third time, the Queen's trip to Ghana went ahead in 1961. It was a state visit not without its controversies or dangers — there was concern at home about violence in the capital, Accra, and the regime's growing ties with the Soviet Union — but the Queen was not to be deterred. "I am the head of the Commonwealth," she said at the time, "and I am paid to face any risks that may be involved"

Motherhood and monarchy

Beneath the Queen's sometimes distant demeanour was a woman who loved her children dearly and maintained strong bonds with them throughout her life, the royal biographer Sally Bedell Smith writes

When she acceded to the throne at 25, Queen Elizabeth was already the mother of three-year-old Prince Charles and 18-month-old Princess Anne. Her one adjustment to the routine of her father, King George VI, was to change the time for the weekly audience with the prime minister from 5.30pm to 6.30pm, allowing her to join the children for their bath and bedtime.

Thus began a lifetime of combining service to her country with her role as a parent, every bit of it under a scrutinising public eye. Like any mother, she had her share of missteps, dramas and rifts with her children. And like all children, they turned out not quite as she might have expected or planned. However, if one moment sums up the Queen's legacy as a mother and the reciprocal love of her children it was during the Diamond Jubilee concert in 2012, when Charles addressed her in front of 18,000 people in a grandstand outside Buckingham Palace, with another 500,000 watching on screens in St James's Park, The Mall and Hyde Park. "Your Majesty, Mummy," he said, drawing an unusually huge public smile from her and great cheers from the crowds. Then he thanked her "for inspiring us with your selfless duty and service, and for making us proud to be British".

From the outset of her reign, the Queen felt it essential to demonstrate her gravitas to the older men who advised her. As a career woman, she was an anomaly in her generation and in the British upper class, without any ready role model. She waited ten years before having her third child, Prince Andrew. Four years later, in 1964, Prince Edward was born.

"Nothing, but nothing deflected her from duty," said Sir Edward Ford, an assistant private secretary to the Queen. "She'd go into labour and have a baby so we knew we weren't going to see her for a while. But within a very short time, 24 or 48 hours, she'd be asking if there were any papers and would we care to send them up?"

She took extended trips too; her first big tour of Commonwealth countries in 1953 and 1954 kept her away from Charles and Anne for nearly six months. Her children were fortunate to have a nurturing nanny in Mabel Anderson. Their maternal grandmother was also an important force who particularly doted on Charles, sometimes to the point of cosseting.

Clarissa Eden, the wife of the prime minister Anthony Eden, was perplexed that the Queen and Queen Mother failed to discipline a six-year-old Charles during a picnic at Windsor Castle when he refused to yield his chair to her husband.

The Queen's children knew that she spent long hours in her office at Buckingham Palace. While she certainly loved her children, she fell into professional habits that pulled her away from motherhood, and missed out on many maternal challenges, as well as pleasures. "She let things go," said Gay Charteris, the wife of Sir Martin Charteris, the Queen's longtime private secretary. "She did have work every day. It was easier to go back to that than children having tantrums. She always had the excuse of the [ministerial] red boxes."

ABOVE
Prince Charles kissing his mother's hand as she presents him with a prize at the Guards Polo Club in Windsor in 1985

TIM GRAHAM/GETTY IMAGES; PA

"She was not a hugger," Lady Mary Clayton, a first cousin of the Queen, said. "She has a different nature."

The Queen was more visibly engaged with her second set of children. When Miss Anderson took time off, the Queen felt relaxed enough to stay in the nursery with Andrew and Edward, tying on an apron for their baths and lulling them to sleep. On weekends at Windsor Castle the boys zoomed down the gilded Grand Corridor in their pedal cars, and if they fell off their bicycles on a gravel path in the park, Andrew recalled, the Queen would pick them up and say, "'Don't be so silly. There's nothing wrong with you. Go and wash off,' just like any parent." At weekend teatimes she joined them to watch the BBC's *Grandstand* sports programme and the Sunday cricket league.

All four children found common ground with their parents during holidays at the family's rural estates, Sandringham and Balmoral. The Queen and Prince Philip taught them to shoot, as well as how to cast into the pools of the River Dee and catch salmon with a well-tied fly. They stalked stags at Balmoral and spent hours on horseback there and at Sandringham. It was in the countryside, away from the pressures of duty, that the Queen bonded best with her children.

The Queen cultivated a love of country pursuits in her grandchildren too. By the time they were teenagers, Prince William and Prince Harry were regulars on the Scottish grouse moors and at Sandringham for pheasant shoots.

The pressure of her duties prompted the Queen to make Philip the ultimate arbiter in decisions about the children. He enforced discipline and selected their schools, which in the case of Charles reflected Philip's belief in the merit of his own experience rather than what was appropriate for his diffident, sensitive eldest son. Charles hated Gordonstoun, in a remote corner of Scotland, although his brothers thrived there, not least because by then the atmosphere was more humane. Anne,

ABOVE
*Prince Andrew at
the handle of the
pram rocks Prince
Edward, watched
by the Queen,
Princess Anne,
Prince Charles
and the Duke of
Edinburgh, in 1965*

whose assertiveness mirrored her father's personality, did well at Benenden, in Kent.

Particularly with her two elder children, the Queen believed in the necessity of exposing them to challenging situations and talking to them "on level, grown-up terms". Mary Wilson, the wife of the prime minister Harold Wilson, remembered "the patience Prince Charles showed when he was around all those adults". The royal children may have grown up in a bubble, but the Queen wanted them to work through difficulties and learn to think for themselves.

"I learnt the way a monkey learns — by watching its parents," Charles once said. During Anne's trip to New Zealand with her parents in 1970, the walkabout was introduced into the royal routine; a casual stroll to chat and shake hands with ordinary people. "At 19 years old, suddenly being dropped in the middle of the street," Anne recalled, "being told to pick someone and talk to them. Fun? No, I don't think so."

Anne had a strong bond with her mother through horses, especially when she became a top competitor in three-day eventing. In 1973, at 23, she married Captain Mark Phillips, an accomplished horseman with an Olympic gold medal.

The Queen's laissez-faire attitude led to unfortunate consequences when her children reached adulthood. Andrew initially showed traits to make his mother proud. He distinguished himself as a helicopter pilot and saw combat during the Falklands conflict in 1982. On his return the Queen appeared to wipe away tears at the flag-waving homecoming at Portsmouth, even as her second son light-heartedly greeted her with a red rose between his teeth. She was genuinely pleased in 1986 when he married Sarah Ferguson, a robust, jolly girl who shared the monarch's love of riding and other country pursuits.

Edward, who had his mother's shy streak, struggled after earning his degree at the University of Cambridge, bailing out of training as a Royal Marine and stumbling in trying to establish himself as a TV producer. He found his footing when he teamed up with his father in running the Duke of Edinburgh's Award scheme for young people. Edward's marriage to Sophie Rhys-Jones, a middle-class public relations consultant, drew him closer to his mother. "Sophie first of all respects her as the Queen, then as a mother-in-law, but she also understands that she is a

human being," said Lady Elizabeth Anson, the Queen's cousin.

The Queen "allowed Prince Charles to work at his interests, his aims and his ambitions", said Sir Malcolm Ross, a senior adviser. "It is not a cosy relationship," said Margaret Rhodes, a cousin. "They love each other, but the family is not set up to be cosy." The absence of cosiness made the marital break-ups that three of the Queen's children went through more difficult for her to recognise and understand, especially that of Charles and Diana, Princess of Wales. "I think it took a long time to accept that the faults were not more his than hers," said Lady Brabourne, a godmother to Charles. In 1992, when Anne, Charles and Andrew split from their spouses, their mother found it "nonplussing", Lady Brabourne recalled. "You don't know how to behave when someone is making such a mess. You want to help them mend, but how to do it?"

The publication in 1994 of Charles's official biography drove a wedge between the heir and his parents. The author, Jonathan Dimbleby, quoted his complaints that the Queen had been remote during his childhood and that Philip had been overbearing and insensitive. His siblings rebuked Charles to his face. A decade later, after another book that elaborated on the themes, Anne countered that "it just beggars belief" to suggest that her mother was aloof and uncaring. Anne said she and her brothers appreciated being "allowed to find our own way... People have to make their own mistakes. I think she's always accepted that."

That approach foundered when Prince Andrew showed shockingly poor judgment by befriending the convicted paedophile Jeffrey Epstein. When the magnitude of his misbehaviour became clear, the Queen had no choice but to remove the prince from public duties. For a mother in her nineties, it was a heartbreaking decision.

Elizabeth's role as matriarch was to preside over a royal family committed to public service. She endeavoured to instil in her children the values and traditions essential to the institution she led. Yet when any of them violated those principles, she had the courage to do what was essential — calling for Charles and Diana to divorce in 1995, and exiling Andrew a quarter of a century later. Her actions reflected the defining principle of the royal family expressed by Lord Stamfordham, private secretary to King George V: "Not as a mere figurehead, but as a living powerful good, affecting the interests and social wellbeing of all classes."

1970s

COMMONWEALTH QUANDARIES AND HER SILVER JUBILEE

LICHFIELD ARCHIVE, CORBIS, SERGE LEMOINE/GETTY IMAGES

In 1970 royal tours underwent a revolution. Until then they had consisted of the Queen travelling somewhere, usually by car, then getting out and meeting whomever she was supposed to meet. There was little spontaneity, and not much chance for the public to see her other than by waving at the royal car as it passed.

Then the royal walkabout was born. It started in New Zealand, where the authorities wanted to find a new format for events that would allow the public more involvement. In Wellington they arranged for the royal limousine to stop short of an engagement so the couple could complete the journey on foot. It went down very well, and in Australia the Queen was keen to try it again. However, in Melbourne she faced an unruly crowd blocking her path. What should I do, she asked a member of staff. "Walk, Your Majesty," they replied. "She faced the crowd and walked and they let her through. It was after that we learnt that we had to use crash barriers."

Five years later political events in Australia would lead to one of the most enduring controversies of her reign. Gough Whitlam's government had been rocked by scandals and by a worsening economic crisis. After he failed to pass a budget and then opted not to resign or call an election, the governor-general, Sir John Kerr — the Queen's representative — dismissed him in November 1975. The move was hugely divisive, and threw a spotlight on the Queen's constitutional powers.

❝

'I am simply amazed,' said the Queen of the crowds at her Silver Jubilee celebrations. 'I had no idea'

It also helped to fuel the republican movement in Australia.

The same year Buckingham Palace started preparations for the Queen's Silver Jubilee, which would take place two years later. They were aware that few people knew what a jubilee was, and were not convinced that there would be much interest. The wave of enthusiasm that swept the country took everyone by surprise, not least the Queen.

The evening before the main celebrations the Queen lit a bonfire in Windsor that would set off a chain of beacons across the country. Afterwards she was driven to London. The crowds along the route grew larger and larger until, at the end of The Mall, the car could barely turn into Buckingham Palace.

"I am simply amazed," the Queen said throughout the celebrations. "I had no idea."

In 1979 the IRA murdered Lord Mountbatten with a bomb in his fishing boat off the coast of Sligo. The Queen was devastated. Later, while Mountbatten's daughter Patricia — one of her oldest friends, who had also been on the boat — remained in hospital, the Queen invited Patricia's 14-year-old son, Timothy Knatchbull, injured in the blast, and his sister Amanda to Balmoral. He later remembered "a strange warm glow that's never really left me... the care, the tender loving care that the Queen [has] as a mum".

Three months later, in November, Margaret Thatcher unmasked the art historian Anthony Blunt in the House of Commons as a former Soviet spy. The Queen stripped him of his knighthood a short while later. She had been told about his betrayal shortly after he confessed to MI5 in 1964. In return for his confession, MI5 agreed to keep his spying a secret and granted him immunity from prosecution. After the Queen was told, the Palace asked what it should do about Blunt, who had been surveyor of the Queen's pictures since 1945. They were advised that he should stay put because any action might alert his former Russian controllers. He remained in post until 1972.

Valentine Low

The Queen, the Duke of Edinburgh and their children in the gardens of Balmoral during the family's summer break in Scotland in 1972. This was one of a series of portraits taken by Patrick Lichfield, the Queen's first cousin once removed, to mark the couple's silver wedding anniversary

ABOVE

On a trip that was part of the 1976 bicentennial celebrations of the American Revolution, the Queen danced at a White House dinner with her host, Gerald Ford, the US president

ABOVE

The Queen on a state visit to Mexico in 1975. Years later the Countess of Wessex explained the Queen's fondness for bright outfits. "She needs to stand out," she said, "for people to be able to say, 'I saw the Queen'" »

Princess Anne and the Queen keep warm in parkas during a visit to Tuktoyaktuk in the Northwest Territories of Canada, part of a ten-day royal tour in July 1970

ABOVE

The Queen interrupted her holiday at Balmoral to meet the American president Richard Nixon and his wife, Pat, accompanied by her prime minister Edward Heath, left, at Chequers in Buckinghamshire, 1970

ABOVE

Despite a bomb threat, Her Majesty, wearing the Diamond Diadem, made her way to Westminster on November 2, 1971, to deliver the Queen's Speech at the state opening of parliament ➤

The Queen and her husband aboard the Royal Yacht Britannia in March 1972 — another in the series of Patrick Lichfield shots marking the couple's 25th wedding anniversary

ABOVE
Prince Edward listens attentively as the Queen explains the details of the Trooping the Colour ceremony outside Buckingham Palace in 1972

ABOVE
Waving goodbye to Fiji during her royal Silver Jubilee tour to the Pacific Islands, New Zealand and Australia in 1977 »

RIGHT
To mark 25 years on the throne, the Queen not only travelled extensively in the UK, visiting 36 counties, but also further afield to Commonwealth countries, taking in Fiji, Tonga, Papua New Guinea, Australia, Canada and parts of the Caribbean, among other destinations. Here, the royal couple receive a group of Fijian folk dancers aboard the Royal Yacht Britannia in February 1977

RIGHT
The Queen, wearing a traditional feather cloak, meets a group of Maoris in New Zealand — or Aotearoa — during her two-week visit in February and March 1977

ABOVE
The Queen, sitting next to Prince Edward, chats to her eldest sons as they watch an event at the 1976 Montreal Olympic Games on July 19. Two days earlier she had officially opened the Games

RIGHT
On November 2, 1977, the Queen returned to London on Concorde from Barbados, the final stop of the West Indies leg of her Silver Jubilee tour — it was not just the supersonic plane's first trip to that island, but also the Queen's first Concorde flight »

Princess Margaret, who had a house on Mustique, welcomes her sister to the Caribbean island in her Silver Jubilee year, 1977

The Queen, Prince Philip, Prince Andrew and the Queen Mother are joined by Princess Margaret, the Earl of Snowdon and their daughter, Lady Sarah Armstrong-Jones, at Badminton in 1973 »

ABOVE
At the Guards Polo Club in Windsor, with the Duke of Edinburgh, who was the founder and president of the club, and was umpiring a polo match on this occasion, June 1973

RIGHT
As part of a tour of the Gulf states in February 1979, the Queen and Prince Philip travelled by Concorde to Riyadh, Saudi Arabia

TIM GRAHAM, MIKE STEPHENS, GRAHAM WILTSHIRE/GETTY IMAGES

ABOVE
The Queen watches Virginia Wade hold the Venus Rosewater Dish aloft after her 4-6, 6-3, 6-1 victory over Betty Stove in the 1977 Wimbledon final. Until Emma Raducanu's triumph at the US Open in 2021, this was the last time a British woman won a grand slam singles title

LEFT
A Silver Jubilee walkabout in Camberwell, south London, in June 1977

The weekly audience with her prime minister

The Queen's 15 heads of government were as different as the challenges they faced, but she remained constant — prepared, thoughtful and astute, writes the Times royal correspondent, Valentine Low

Despite the entertaining fantasy promulgated by Peter Morgan in his play *The Audience*, no one really knew what was discussed during the weekly meetings between the Queen and the prime minister. Plenty of people have asked, however. In the early days of her reign, when the Queen was in her twenties and Winston Churchill was more than half a century her senior, his private secretary Jock Colville noticed that as the two of them grew to know each other, the meetings got longer. "What do you talk about?" he asked the prime minister. "Oh, mostly racing," he replied.

For all his jocularity, it would be a mistake to suppose that the meetings were all gossip and small talk. She read her boxes and always knew what was going on. "The Queen," Edward Heath wrote, "is undoubtedly one of the best-informed people in the world."

Her 14th prime minister was Boris Johnson — who was four months old when her fifth prime minister, Harold Wilson, came to power. Inevitably the Queen got on better with some of her prime ministers than others, and one suspects that her relationship with Johnson struggled to recover after he asked her to prorogue parliament in 2019 only for the advice to be ruled unlawful.

Churchill adored her and occupied a special place in her affections; the historian Ben Pimlott described how the meetings would take on an almost jaunty air. "The premier would arrive wearing a frock coat and top hat, with a gleam in his eye, and disappear happily into a secret conclave."

Harold Macmillan treated their relationship as what Pimlott called a kind of "chivalrous fantasy", while she got on surprisingly well with Wilson, despite having little in common with him. He treated her as an equal, and aides noted that their audiences grew longer. He once

> ## Even the most socially adept of prime ministers could be put in their place

described the meetings as the only times when he could have a serious conversation, which would not be leaked, with somebody who wasn't after his job.

Not all of the relationships have been quite so easy. When Heath met her, he said: "I lost my nerve and said to her, 'Have you been busy lately, Ma'am?' 'That,' she replied, 'is the sort of question lord mayors ask when I visit cities.'" Heath had no small talk and little time for women, and as a member of the household observed: "The Queen found Heath hard going."

Politically, too, they were at odds: she was a fervent believer in the Commonwealth, while Heath was a passionate European to the exclusion of all else. In 1971 he wanted her to stay away from the first Commonwealth leaders' meeting in Singapore because of the anticipated furious reaction to his plan to resume arms sales to South Africa; it took an intense meeting between monarch and prime minister for her to agree.

Even the most socially adept of prime ministers could be put in their place. Recalling his first audience, Tony Blair said: "She was… direct. 'You are my tenth prime minister. The first was Winston. That was before you were born.' I got a sense of my relative seniority, or lack of it."

Margaret Thatcher was her longest-

serving prime minister and, in terms of the relationship between monarch and politician, the most contentious. The two women were different in both their politics and their personal style. Thatcher was no countrywoman and struggled with her annual visit to Balmoral; more importantly, they never saw eye to eye over the importance of the Commonwealth. Yet the furore that was caused by an article in *The Sunday Times* that said the Queen was dismayed by some of Thatcher's policies probably led to an exaggerated view about the level of animosity between them. The Queen had a profound respect for Thatcher and attended her funeral — a state funeral in all but name.

As the Queen grew older, and her prime ministers younger, their relationship changed. When John Major — the first prime minister who was younger than the Queen — succeeded Thatcher, the Queen "discovered in him a more relaxed congenial visitor than his predecessor", according to Pimlott.

David Cameron, whose brother used to go to tea at Windsor because he was at prep school with Prince Edward, revealed how she occasionally teased him. Although she never saw *The Audience*, she got wind of the scene in which she supposedly dozes off as Cameron bores her with the latest political machinations from Europe. Later, the [real] Queen told him that she had never fallen asleep during their weekly meetings. After a dramatic pause, she added: "Yet!"

The Scottish independence referendum of 2014 illustrated just how closely the Palace works hand in hand with Downing Street. The No campaign, which was fighting to

keep Scotland part of the United Kingdom, was always expected to win but as voting day approached the Yes campaign started to catch up and the two sides were running neck and neck. No 10 got into a panic, and approached the Palace to see if there was anything that could be done to help. As Cameron put it, he was not asking "for anything that would be in any way improper or unconstitutional but just a raising of the eyebrow even, you know, a quarter of an inch, we thought would make a difference".

The result was a carefully plotted intervention — engineered by Sir Jeremy Heywood, the cabinet secretary, and Sir Christopher Geidt, the Queen's private secretary — in which the Queen stopped to talk to members of the public after going to church near Balmoral. She told one: "I hope people will think very carefully about the future." It was cleverly worded: there was nothing political in what she said, but everyone knew what she meant.

After the No campaign won, Cameron was picked up on a microphone saying that the Queen had "purred down the line" when he gave her the news. He later apologised for his indiscretion. "It was very, very stupid of me," he said. "Oh, it was terrible. Anyway, I apologised, grovelled a lot."

Of the Queen's relationship with Gordon Brown, almost nothing is known. However, he did provide one of the more amusing prime ministerial moments of her reign, when he appeared to get lost at a state banquet after walking the wrong way round the banqueting table. "Has the prime minister got lost?" the Queen asked. "He disappeared the wrong way at the crucial moment."

ABOVE
Boris Johnson meets the Queen for their first weekly audience after Covid-19 restrictions lift, in June 2021

ABOVE LEFT
Princess Elizabeth with Winston Churchill, the leader of the opposition, in 1950. Two years later, when she became Queen, he was her first prime minister. Clement Attlee and his wife, Violet, look on

LEFT
The Queen with Tony Blair at Buckingham Palace in 2002

TIM GRAHAM, KEYSTONE/
CORBIS/GETTY IMAGES;
DOMINIC LIPINSKI/PA

Her relationship with Johnson got off to an uncertain start when the new prime minister let slip after their first meeting that she told him: "I don't know why anyone would want the job." Such indiscretion might have been forgiven: what was more serious was when he advised the Queen to prorogue parliament in what was seen by many as an unconstitutional attempt to avoid parliamentary scrutiny of the government's Brexit plans in the final weeks before Britain's withdrawal from the EU. The advice was later ruled unlawful by the Supreme Court. However the Queen felt about it, the Duke of Cambridge for one was said to have been unhappy that the monarchy had been put into such an awkward situation.

If that was not bad enough, Downing Street also had to apologise to the Palace over two leaving parties held in apparent breach of coronavirus lockdown rules on the night before the Duke of Edinburgh's socially distanced funeral.

By the time Johnson resigned as Conservative leader in 2022 the Queen was having problems with her mobility. When it came time for him to hand over to his successor, Liz Truss, the Queen was at Balmoral, and decided not to make the journey to London; instead, Truss became the first prime minister to be appointed at Balmoral since the Marquess of Salisbury in 1885. Two days later she announced the Queen's death.

While it is certain that the Queen never showed the slightest inclination to interfere in politics — aside, it might be argued, from her intervention in the Scottish referendum — she found on a number of occasions that

it was hard to avoid. During the Suez crisis of 1956 she was in the invidious position of being kept thoroughly informed, thanks to a stream of Foreign Office papers and telegrams. So much so that she knew more of what was happening than a number of ministers, some of whom were notoriously kept in the dark. It also put her in a dilemma with regard to the Commonwealth: did she tell Commonwealth leaders what she had been told in confidence, or did she betray their trust by withholding information that was relevant to their interests?

As for the Queen's position on Anthony Eden's Suez intervention, it seems she was not entirely neutral. "I think the Queen believed Eden was mad," one Palace aide recalled.

One of the most controversial episodes in the Queen's political life came during the resignation of Macmillan as prime minister in 1963. This was before the Conservative Party elected its leaders; the new leader was supposed to emerge through soundings, although there was no agreed mechanism as to how the process should work.

Chaos ensued, with the leading contenders jockeying for position, the cabinet divided and backbench MPs throwing in their two ha'p'orth. Macmillan, recovering from a prostate operation but determined to mastermind the changeover from his hospital bed, was doing everything in his power to ensure that the obvious candidate — Rab Butler, the deputy prime minister — did not get the job.

He managed to organise it so that within three quarters of an hour of his eventual resignation, the Queen was at his hospital bedside for a farewell meeting. She asked him for his advice, he suggested that she call for Lord Home (who would later relinquish his title to become Sir Alec Douglas-Home) and she agreed. According to Pimlott, the advice was unconstitutional, although it may have been what she wanted to hear.

The controversy caused by the selection process led to a change in Tory party rules. It also explains why, when the Queen faced another constitutionally tricky moment — the 2010 general election, which was widely expected not to produce a party with an overall majority — she ensured that her private secretary had done a thorough job of laying the groundwork with the cabinet secretary, so when the time came for the post-election horse-trading to choose a prime minister, a clearly defined process was agreed and set in place. She was not going to be caught out again.

1980s

A ROYAL SOAP OPERA

The 1980s was the starting point for two of Britain's better-known soap operas, *Brookside* on Channel 4 and *EastEnders* on BBC1. For the royal family, it was the start of the soap opera years, with the antics of the younger members of the family keeping the tabloid press fed with a regular diet of front-page stories.

The undoubted highlight of the decade was the marriage of Prince Charles and Lady Diana Spencer at St Paul's Cathedral on July 29, 1981, when Diana became the first Englishwoman to marry an heir to the throne for 300 years. The grandeur of the occasion — the couple chose St Paul's because it could seat more guests than Westminster Abbey — and the willingness of the public to be caught up in the romance were rendered hollow by the sheer unpleasantness of the couple's break-up as their marriage began to unravel a few years later.

Five years after Charles and Diana's wedding Prince Andrew married Sarah Ferguson at Westminster Abbey. Their marriage did not fare much better, although the couple remained friends long after their divorce.

Six weeks before Charles and Diana's wedding the Queen had shown her coolness under pressure when six shots were fired at her as she rode down The Mall during Trooping the Colour. Her horse, Burmese, bolted but within a few paces she had got the animal back under control. Leaning forward, she patted the frightened horse's neck to calm him down. The shots were later discovered to be blanks. The culprit, 17-year-old Marcus Sarjeant, was

66
The Queen showed her coolness under pressure when six shots were fired at her during Trooping the Colour

sentenced to five years in prison under the Treason Act 1842, and released after three.

The Queen showed similar sangfroid in the summer of 1982 when she woke up one morning to discover an intruder in her bedroom. He was Michael Fagan, and he had broken into the palace before. The first time he left without being caught, but on July 9 he woke up the Queen by drawing the curtains before sitting down on her bed.

As she later told her press secretary Michael Shea: "I got out of bed, put on my dressing gown, drew myself up to my full regal height, pointed to the door and said, 'Get out!' — and he didn't." She pressed the alarm and twice tried calling a policeman for help. It was only when she got him into the corridor that she managed to summon assistance. Fagan later spent three months in a psychiatric hospital.

Shea found himself in hot water in July 1986 when *The Sunday Times* ran a front-page story saying that the Queen found the prime minister Margaret Thatcher's approach often to be "uncaring, confrontational and socially divisive". The story, based on briefings by "sources close to the Queen", also stated that she disapproved of Downing Street's policy towards apartheid in South Africa because it threatened to split the Commonwealth. Buckingham Palace retorted that "reports purporting to be the Queen's opinion of government policies are entirely without foundation".

Although Shea initially denied it, he eventually admitted being the main source of the story. While *The Sunday Times* believed the briefings reflected views within the royal family, there was no indication that Shea had spoken at the Queen's behest. He left the Palace a few months later.

The nadir of the decade came in 1987 with *It's a Royal Knockout*, a charity event organised by Prince Edward. The Queen was said to disapprove, but Edward pushed on, with the help of fellow team captains Princess Anne and the Duke and Duchess of York. Widely regarded since as embarrassing, the event is remembered for Edward storming out of a press conference after journalists failed to show sufficient enthusiasm.

Valentine Low

TOP
Accompanied by the prime minister Margaret Thatcher, Her Majesty is invited to Whitehall to unveil a statue of the 1st Earl Mountbatten of Burma in November 1983. The earl was killed by an IRA bomb on his boat in Co Sligo in 1979

ABOVE
Lady Diana Spencer and Prince Charles pose with the Queen on March 27, 1981, the day that their wedding was sanctioned by the privy council

LEFT
The Queen and Prince Philip tour the Badaling section of the Great Wall on their first and only state visit to China in 1986. The Queen was the first British monarch to visit the country, and her six-day trip signified a strengthening of relations before the handover of Hong Kong to China in 1997 »

FAR LEFT
The monarch takes a snap of Prince Philip with her Leica camera at the Royal Windsor Horse Show, May 1982. She wears the Cullinan V diamond heart brooch for the occasion

LEFT
The Queen calms her horse as police spring into action after a man in the crowd fires blanks from a replica pistol during Trooping the Colour in London, June 1981

ABOVE
Charles and Diana share their famous kiss on the balcony of Buckingham Palace on their wedding day, July 29, 1981

RIGHT
The Queen, the Queen Mother and Princess Margaret pose in matching Hardy Amies blue satin outfits for an official Norman Parkinson portrait to mark the Queen Mother's 80th birthday in 1980 »

ABOVE
In Portsmouth Queen Elizabeth joins a huge crowd to welcome home the aircraft carrier HMS Invincible and its crewmen, including her son Prince Andrew, after serving in the Falklands conflict, 1982

LEFT
The Queen presents the Order of Merit to Mother Teresa at the presidential palace in New Delhi, India, in November 1983

RIGHT
The Queen cheers the winner of the 1989 Epsom Derby, with Prince and Princess Michael of Kent. It's one event in the racing calendar that her own horses have never won ≫

ABOVE
From Funafuti on the Polynesian island of Tuvalu, the Queen is carried into the water on a local canoe to return to the Royal Yacht Britannia in October 1982

LEFT
The Queen jumps aboard for a brief ride in a commercial bus on the outskirts of Acapulco, Mexico, during an official visit in February 1983

LEFT
The US president Ronald Reagan is amused at a joke by the Queen at a dinner in San Francisco in March 1983. She alluded to the disappointing Californian weather she had endured since her arrival on American shores

TOP
The Queen takes an interest in a pig during a visit to the Festival of Food and Farming in Hyde Park, London, May 1989

ABOVE
Teaching Prince Harry, left, and Prince William the finer points of polo in the royal box at the Guards Polo Club, Windsor, June 1987 »

LEFT
The Queen held three garden parties every year at Buckingham Palace, plus one at the Palace of Holyroodhouse in Edinburgh, when guests from all walks of life could spend the afternoon mingling on the lawns. After the Queen stopped receiving debutantes in 1958, a practice that was deemed out of touch, garden parties were the place to be presented to her, and by the 1980s had become established as a way of recognising and rewarding public service. Here, the Queen, in an emerald green outfit, bottom left, greets invitees

Corgis, a Queen's best friend

Whether she was on duty or off, the Queen liked to keep her dogs close, writes the Times royal correspondent, Valentine Low

The Queen's corgis were an instantly recognisable part of her public image. From newspaper cartoons to the video she made with Daniel Craig for the 2012 London Olympics, when a corgi appeared the Queen was never far behind. They even played a crucial role in kick-starting the plot in Alan Bennett's literary fantasy about the Queen, *The Uncommon Reader*.

Yet for all the Queen's devotion to her corgis — and her dorgis, a corgi-dachshund cross — it would be wrong to think that she was a one-breed woman.

There were labradors too, and spaniels; the Queen took an active interest in the Sandringham kennels and was regarded as a highly proficient handler of gundogs.

Her first dog, however, the one that inspired her love of animals, was a Cairn terrier, given to her by her uncle the Prince of Wales, the future Edward VIII. Princess Elizabeth was three years old at the time.

Her first corgi was Dookie, bought by her father, George VI, in 1933. Generation after generation of them followed. One of the most notable was Susan, the matriarch of the dynasty. On Elizabeth's wedding day, when she and Prince Philip were driven in an open carriage from Buckingham Palace to Waterloo station for the start of their honeymoon, Susan travelled with them, snuggled up under a rug. At Waterloo she stole the show by tumbling out first on to the red carpet.

Susan produced Sugar and Honey, while they in turn led to Whisky and Sherry — Sugar's offspring — and Bee; over the years the Queen had more than 30 corgis.

Being a royal pet was, naturally, not a life short of privilege. At Buckingham Palace the dogs slept in their own room, in wicker baskets raised off the floor to avoid draughts. Whenever she could, the Queen exercised, fed and groomed them herself; it is said that if she entered a room wearing a headscarf

they sensed that a walk was imminent and would scamper about excitedly.

The former royal chef Darren McGrady, who worked for the Queen for 11 years, described how the corgis would be served only the finest fare. "One day it would be chuck steak, which we boiled and served with finely chopped boiled cabbage and white rice. The next they'd have poached chicken or liver. Or rabbits shot by William or Harry."

If the dogs could be unruly, it seemed to be just the way the Queen liked it. "They chase rabbits like mad," the Queen's cousin Margaret Rhodes said. "There are a lot of rabbits around Balmoral, certainly, and the Queen gets excited with the dogs chasing the rabbits, egging them on." There could be trouble, though. Susan bit the royal clock winder and attacked one of the palace sentries. Another bit a policeman.

In her later years the Queen stopped breeding corgis because she did not want to leave any behind when she died. The last of her corgi dynasty, Willow — the 14th generation descended from Susan — died in April 2018. "She has mourned every one of her corgis over the years, but she has been more upset about Willow's death than any of them," a source said. "It is probably because Willow was the last link to her parents and a pastime that goes back to her own childhood."

The Queen still had her dorgi, Candy, and was not without corgis for long. In 2021, while the Duke of Edinburgh was in hospital, the Duke of York and his daughters, Princess Beatrice and Princess Eugenie, gave her two puppies — Fergus, a dorgi who was named after her uncle, and Muick, a corgi named after one of her favourite Scottish beauty spots, Loch Muick. After Fergus died aged five months, the Yorks gave her another corgi puppy, Sandy, on what would have been Philip's 100th birthday.

LEFT
Enjoying the Scottish countryside, the Queen and Prince Philip on an outing with a bevy of corgis at Balmoral in 1994

FAR LEFT, TOP
Princess Elizabeth, aged ten, with her corgis Jane and Dookie at home in London in 1936

FAR LEFT, CENTRE
At Virginia Water watching competitors, including Prince Philip, driving at the Royal Windsor Horse Show in 1973

FAR LEFT, BOTTOM
The Queen with one of her corgis returning from Balmoral in 1986

1990s

CRISIS AND TRAGEDY

On November 20, 1992, at about 11.15am, a fire started in the private chapel of Windsor Castle when a spotlight was pressed up against a curtain. By the time the fire services arrived it was too late to save the chapel: the fire took hold in the roof, spread along the rafters to other parts of the building and ended up damaging or destroying more than 100 rooms, including most of St George's Hall. The Queen was devastated. As one of her private secretaries said: "I don't think I've really seen her so emotionally affected by anything as much as the Windsor fire."

It had been a bad year for the Queen. Prince Andrew and his wife, Sarah, had separated in March, while Princess Anne divorced Captain Mark Phillips the next month. The disintegration of Charles and Diana's marriage had been laid bare by the serialisation in *The Sunday Times* in June of Andrew Morton's book *Diana: Her True Story*. As if all that wasn't enough, eggs were thrown at the Queen during a state visit to Germany.

The fire led to a row over who should pay for the restoration of Windsor Castle, which, on government advice, had not been insured. There was public outrage when the government announced that it would foot the bill, which caught the Palace by surprise. In the end it was funded by charging the public for admission to Windsor and Buckingham Palace, augmented by donations and £2 million of the Queen's own money.

To try to limit the damage to her reputation, an announcement that the Queen would start to pay income tax for the first time in her reign was brought forward. It had long been in the planning, but as an exercise in PR spin the change of timing did not do much good: as the joint authors of one book remarked, "It looked as though she was running scared from the public."

Four days after the fire at Windsor Castle, with a heavy cold that was exacerbated by smoke from the blaze, the Queen gave a speech marking her 40 years on the throne. "1992 is not a year on which I shall look back with undiluted pleasure," she said, with regal understatement. "In the words of one of my more sympathetic correspondents, it has turned out to be an annus horribilis." A phrase was born.

More was to come that year. In December Charles and Diana formally separated, and the year ended with the Queen suing *The Sun* newspaper for breach of copyright when it published the text of her annual Christmas message two days before it was broadcast.

In August 1997, a year after her divorce from Charles, Diana was killed in a car crash in Paris. Her death sparked an extraordinary wave of public mourning, and of criticism of the royal family. By remaining at Balmoral, where she was doing her best to protect 15-year-old William, and 12-year-old Harry, the Queen appeared distant and uncaring. A decision, later rescinded, not to fly the Union flag at half-mast over Buckingham Palace — correct according to precedent but out of tune with public sentiment —made matters worse.

The wave of antiroyal feeling only abated when the Queen came to London and spoke to members of the public outside Buckingham Palace. That evening she gave a broadcast from the Chinese Dining Room. With the crowds visible through the window behind her, she spoke of her sense of loss and shock, and described Diana as "an exceptional and gifted human being". The broadcast also included a phrase put in at the suggestion of Tony Blair: "What I say to you now, as your Queen and as a grandmother, I say from my heart…"

She was praised for her sincerity. But it would take a long time for the royal family to recover.
Valentine Low

> 66
> The Queen spoke of her sense of loss and shock, and described Diana as 'an exceptional and gifted human being'

PETER MARLOW/MAGNUM PHOTOS

The funeral of Diana, Princess of Wales took place on September 6, 1997. The previous evening the Queen gave a televised address to the nation to express the royal family's shock and sadness >>

ABOVE
The Queen outside Clarence House in August 1990, marking the 90th birthday of the Queen Mother, centre. They are joined by, from left, Prince Edward, the Princess and Prince of Wales and Princess Margaret

LEFT
Rain fails to dampen the spirits of the Queen and the Queen Mother as they arrive for a day's racing at Royal Ascot in June 1997

ABOVE
A quiet moment on the inaugural service of British Rail's InterCity 225 between London and Edinburgh, June 1991

LEFT
Aiming an SA80 rifle to fire the last shot at an Army Rifle Association centenary shoot at Bisley in Surrey, in July 1993 »

The Queen surveys the scene the day after the fire at Windsor Castle. In a huge salvage operation carried out during the blaze, hundreds of items of furniture and works of art were moved to safety

ABOVE
The fire at Windsor Castle burned for 15 hours on November 20 and 21, 1992. The State Apartments, centre left, and Brunswick Tower, centre right, suffered extensive damage — in total 115 rooms were destroyed

LEFT
A visibly emotional Queen was shown around the site by senior officers the next day; the restoration work cost £36.5 million and took five years to complete »

ABOVE
During a tour of America in 1991, the Queen and Prince Philip watch a baseball game in Baltimore with the US president George HW Bush and his wife, Barbara

RIGHT
The Queen looks on as the German national football team's captain Jürgen Klinsmann lifts the trophy at the Euro 1996 championship. His team beat the Czech Republic 2-1 in the final at Wembley

FAR RIGHT
A member of the Manchester United supporters' club in Kuala Lumpur gets the signature "Elizabeth R" on his football during a state visit to Malaysia in 1998

ABOVE
After a raucous encounter with Prince Charles a few months earlier, the Spice Girls were on their best behaviour at this Royal Variety Performance in December 1997

LEFT
Nelson Mandela, the South African president, at Buckingham Palace, where he stayed as a guest of the Queen during his 1996 visit. The two heads of state enjoyed a warm friendship and called each other by their first names »

ABOVE
Four days after the death of Diana, Princess of Wales, her sons are seen with other members of the royal family viewing the floral tributes left for her outside Balmoral

RIGHT
The Queen and Prince Philip with five of their grandchildren at Balmoral in 1999

FAR RIGHT
Her Majesty apears to wipe away a tear as she leaves Diana's funeral service at Westminster Abbey

On September 5, having flown back to London from Balmoral earlier that day, the Queen and Prince Philip survey the sea of flowers left by members of the public at the gates of Buckingham Palace in tribute to Diana, Princess of Wales

The quiet diplomat who could soften the steeliest leaders

Over her lifetime the Queen met hundreds of heads of state and government, impressing each one with her intelligence and knowledge. On the world stage she played her role to perfection, writes the Times royal correspondent, Valentine Low

The Queen fulfilled her international role in a way that no British sovereign had done before. From the youthful dazzle of her first tour as Princess Elizabeth to her immaculate performance for the 2019 state visit by a starstruck Donald Trump, she met many world leaders, and more often than not left them highly impressed.

When the Chinese president Xi Jinping visited in October 2015, the Palace welcome was treated by China as the sort of affirmation that they could get nowhere else. It had been the same in Germany that summer, when Angela Merkel abandoned a meeting on the Greek economy to spend more time with her guest.

Even among the most stellar players on the world stage, the Queen showed a quiet magnetism that remained undiminished — to say nothing of a capacity to surprise. When she and Michelle Obama put their arms around each other at a Buckingham Palace reception in 2009, it showed the Queen to be warmer and more affectionate than some had supposed, and less bound by protocol than those who surrounded her. The bond forged between them paved the way for a successful state visit by President Obama in 2011.

Her capacity to cast a spell over the most important of leaders was seen once more when Trump became US president. He immediately let it be known that what he wanted above all was a state visit to Britain with all the trimmings, including a carriage procession down The Mall. It took two years to agree, and he didn't get the carriage procession he craved, but the visit was a success in a way that few would have dared to hope. It was, he said afterwards, "magnificent", but it was the Queen "who I was most impressed with!"

Some bonds were stronger than others. When Vladimir Putin visited in 2000, he had tea with the Queen at Windsor — a relatively brief visit. Three years later the Russian president paid a state visit that was notable, among other things, for his being 15 minutes late for the ceremonial welcome.

One of her warmest relationships was with Nelson Mandela. The South African president is reported to have called her Elizabeth; she called him Nelson. They got off to a good start long before he was president. Recently released from prison, Mandela had been invited to the 1991 Commonwealth summit in Harare, but, because he was not a head of government, he had not been invited to the Queen's banquet. Her courtiers, unsure what to do, asked her. "Let's have him," she said. They got on, it was said, "like a house on fire".

Mandela even got the Queen to behave in un-Queen-like ways. On his state visit to the UK in 1996 he asked for a concert at the Royal Albert Hall instead of a banquet. When, during the rousing finale, he got up to dance, she did likewise. "Good heavens," one establishment figure said. "The Queen is dancing!"

In an era when we are accustomed to the celebrity status of the Duchess of Sussex and the Duchess of Cambridge, and before

them Diana, Princess of Wales, it is easy to forget that the young Elizabeth had a star quality at least as great. Crowds came out in their thousands to see her, and statesmen fell for her charms. In a postwar world short of glamour there was fanciful talk of the "Faerie Princess". Later, when youth and beauty were no longer the most important weapons in her armoury, she employed her wisdom and experience to useful effect. On more than one occasion the British government owed some of its foreign policy successes to the backstage diplomacy carried out by the Queen.

She won her first international admirers before she became Queen. As Princess Elizabeth, she undertook a tour of Canada in 1951 that included a trip to the US. President Truman was smitten. Afterwards the British ambassador, Sir Oliver Franks, wrote to the king to say that when Truman appeared with her in public, he conveyed "the impression of a very proud uncle presenting his favourite niece to his friends".

His successor, Dwight Eisenhower, became a firm friend. When the Eisenhowers were guests at Balmoral in 1959 he admired some homemade drop scones and she promised to send him the recipe. Later, she wrote to the president: "Seeing a picture of you in today's newspaper standing in front of a barbecue grilling quail reminded me that I had never sent you the recipe of the drop scones which I promised you at Balmoral. I now hasten to do so and I do hope you will find them successful." She concluded: "I think the mixture needs a great deal of beating while making and shouldn't stand around too long before cooking."

Even the Russians were won over. When Nikita Khrushchev visited Britain in 1956, the Communist Party general secretary likened her to "the sort of young woman you'd be likely to meet walking along Gorky Street on a balmy summer afternoon".

When Britain was negotiating to enter the Common Market, the government tried to overcome French objections by inviting Charles de Gaulle for a state visit in 1960. He was given a ceremonial welcome and a state dinner and was delighted that all the royal family came to a banquet at the French embassy. He appreciated the Queen's fluency in French and realised, he wrote, that "she was well informed about everything, that her judgments, on people and events, were as clear-cut as they were thoughtful, that no one was more preoccupied by the cares and problems of our storm-tossed age".

Unfortunately, de Gaulle still said "Non".

For all her triumphs, not every foreign encounter was an unvarnished triumph: her state visit to Morocco in 1980 became known as "the tour from hell". The erratic behaviour of King Hassan II, which included failing to appear for a luncheon until 5pm, infuriated the Queen, who even considered walking out at one point. When he pointed at Robert Fellowes, her assistant private secretary at the time, and said that he was responsible for the "terrible muddle", the Queen rebuked him: "I'll thank you not to speak to my staff like that."

The Queen had to put up with some fairly unsavoury guests. She was uncomfortable entertaining Nicolae Ceausescu, the Romanian leader, during his state visit in 1978; walking her dogs in the gardens at Buckingham Palace, she hid behind a bush rather than converse with the dictator and his wife.

She was most angry with President Mobutu of Zaire, who visited in 1973; his wife smuggled a small dog through customs and ordered it steak from the palace kitchens. The deputy master of the household was told: "Get that dog out of my house!" It was duly consigned to the kennels at Heathrow.

The Queen's great advantage over most elected leaders, certainly all British statesmen, was that she had been around longer than any of them. This proved useful in the Commonwealth crisis of 1979, when African leaders turned against Britain for what they saw as its

DOMINIC LIPINSKI/PA;
TERRY FINCHER/POPPERFOTO/
GETTY IMAGES

ABOVE
President Reagan shared a love of horses with the Queen and went riding with her at Windsor on his visit in 1982

> **"**
> One government official called the Queen 'our secret weapon'

failure to act against Ian Smith's white-minority-ruled Rhodesia.

As the former Commonwealth secretary-general Sir Sonny Ramphal said: "Julius Nyerere [of Tanzania] and Kenneth Kaunda [of Zambia]... were young men when she became Queen, making their way in political life. She knew them as young prime ministers and young presidents and so over many years they were friends."

The Commonwealth heads of government meeting in Lusaka that August, which Margaret Thatcher initially refused to attend, seemed set to be a disaster. "Britain was looked on with the greatest possible distrust," a minister said. Not the Queen, however. When she arrived the government-owned *Zambia Daily Mail* contrasted her "extraordinary loving heart" with Thatcher's lack of sympathy. As head of the Commonwealth, the Queen was seen as transcending national boundaries.

Kaunda recalled a conversation in Lusaka. "She said, 'My friend, you and I should be careful. We are under the scrutiny of the British prime minister.' I looked up and Mrs Thatcher had her eyes fixed on us."

Softened up by the Queen, Kaunda swept Thatcher on to the dancefloor after the opening banquet and the meeting ended with an agreement that led to the negotiations for the peaceful establishment of an independent Zimbabwe.

During the Falklands crisis in 1982 Britain had American support for a military response to Argentina's invasion of the islands, but it was important to strengthen the bond. During a stay at Windsor Castle, President Reagan found the Queen "charming and down-to-earth", and went riding with her in Windsor Home Park. In a speech to parliament, he confirmed his backing for the UK over the Falklands.

In her eighties and nineties the Queen still played an important role. In 2014 she welcomed Michael D Higgins when he became the first president of the Republic of Ireland to pay a state visit to the UK. The next year she played host to President Xi, and in 2018 rolled out the red carpet for Saudi Arabia's crown prince Mohammed bin Salman; controversial visits both, but deemed sufficiently important for the government to wheel out what one official called "our secret weapon".

The important work on these diplomatic events was, perhaps, done behind the scenes. However, it was the Queen, as ever playing her role to perfection, who provided the star quality.

2000s

A NEW MILLENNIUM, AND THE WORK MUST GO ON

Planning was well under way for the Queen's Golden Jubilee in 2002 when she was hit by two personal tragedies in quick succession. On February 9, 2002, Princess Margaret died, after years of ill health. While her passing might not have provoked the great public grieving it would have done when she had been in her heyday, for the Queen the loss of the sister to whom she had been so close was a heavy blow. At the funeral at St George's Chapel, Windsor, as she watched the coffin being lifted into the hearse, she wiped away her tears with a black-gloved hand.

Seven weeks later the Queen Mother died, aged 101. The Queen had been at her side at Royal Lodge, Windsor, along with her cousin Margaret Rhodes and Princess Margaret's children, Viscount Linley and Lady Sarah Chatto.

In the days before the funeral the Queen Mother's coffin was placed on a catafalque in Westminster Hall, where the royal family gathered for prayers. On the drive back to Buckingham Palace, a ripple of applause ran through the crowd and the Queen was cheered all the way up The Mall. It was, she said, one of the most touching things that had happened to her.

With everything that had occurred in the preceding years, the Palace was worried that the jubilee would be a flop. But their fears were misplaced. In what she called "about as full a year as I can remember", Her Majesty embarked on a demanding tour of the UK, visiting 70 towns and cities. There were commemorations and street parties, and in London up to a million people attended each day of the three-day celebration.

"The jubilee has been a most interesting experience," Prince Philip wrote to a friend. "It's impossible not to be stimulated by the enthusiasm of the crowds."

Throughout the early years of the new millennium Charles was pursuing his own agenda — to win both the public and his mother round to Camilla Parker Bowles. It was a long, slow process, with carefully choreographed meetings, leaks to the media and staged public appearances.

Over Christmas 2004 at Sandringham, the Queen, who had long been cautious about the advisability of Charles's remarriage, finally agreed to it. The couple were married the next year in a civil ceremony at the Guildhall in Windsor, which the Queen did not attend. She did, however, attend the subsequent service of prayer and dedication at St George's Chapel. At the reception she seemed noticeably cheerful, and she gave a speech that made witty reference to the fact that the Grand National was being held the same day.

"Having cleared Becher's Brook and the Chair and all kinds of other terrible obstacles, they have come through and I'm very proud and wish them well," she said. "My son is home and dry with the woman he loves. They are now on the home straight; the happy couple are now in the winners' enclosure."

As she entered her eighties, the Queen showed little sign of easing up, her appetite for work remaining as strong as ever.

Valentine Low

> ## " The Queen was cheered all the way up The Mall. It was 'one of the most touching things' that had happened to her

RIGHT
In the Regency Room at Buckingham Palace, the Queen enjoys reading some of the greetings cards sent by members of the public for her 80th birthday, April 21, 2006 »

FIONA HANSON/PA

Ballerinas line a stairway to greet the Queen as she opens the new South Porch of the Royal Albert Hall in 2004, after an eight-year renovation project

ABOVE

On a visit to Elstree Studios in Hertfordshire in 2001, the Queen is shown around the set of the Queen Vic pub by EastEnders cast members Barbara Windsor and Steve McFadden

ABOVE

The party is in full swing at the Millennium Dome in Greenwich, southeast London, as the royal family, joined by Tony and Cherie Blair, usher in the new century with a rendition of Auld Lang Syne

ABOVE

The US president Bill Clinton, his wife, Hillary, and daughter, Chelsea, after tea at Buckingham Palace with the Queen on their three-day trip in 2000 »

TIM GRAHAM, ANWAR HUSSEIN, PAUL J RICHARDS/AFP/GETTY IMAGES; MARTIN SPAVEN/PA

RIGHT
On a tour to Australia in March 2002, the Queen and Prince Philip watch a group of indigenous Tjapukai people light a ceremonial fire during a cultural performance near Cairns. Between 1954 and 2011 the Queen made 16 visits to Australia

TORSTEN BLACKWOOD/EPA; ANWAR HUSSEIN/GETTY IMAGES

LEFT
A swarm of bees disrupts a review of the Grenadier Guards' Queen's Company regiment at Windsor Castle, and the ensuing chaos prompts a fit of the giggles as the Queen passes Prince Philip, who was colonel of the regiment, 2003 »

ANNIE LEIBOVITZ/TRUNK ARCHIVE

LEFT
Photographed by Annie Leibovitz in 2007, Her Majesty stands against a backdrop of the grounds of Buckingham Palace, wearing the Admiral's Cloak, as she wore in earlier portraits by Pietro Annigoni and Cecil Beaton

| 1940s | 1950s | 1960s | 1970s | 1980s | 1990s | 2000s |

Decades of style and colour

The Queen found a way to stand out in a crowd, while still being taken seriously. Her unique feminine style endured for more than seven decades, writes the Times fashion director, Anna Murphy

'If I wore beige," the Queen once said, "nobody would know who I am." Dress head to toe in cerise or turquoise, on the other hand, and there was no question who One might be, no difficulty picking One out in a crowd. At heart Her Majesty's choices were the regal equivalent of the hi-vis jacket, and often almost as bright.

The Queen made up her own rule book when it came to getting dressed. She had to: it was not as if there had been a recent precedent for a female British head of state

1940s　　1950s　　1960s　　1970s　　1980s　　1990s　　2000s

when she inherited the throne in 1952. (Nor will there be a subsequent one; the next three generations in line to the throne are male.)

Aside from her adherence to colour, she had strong views on hats; above all, that she should wear one, but also that the brim should be off the face so as not to inhibit her public getting a clear sightline.

Yet she was hatless when she appeared front row at London Fashion Week in February 2018, presumably so she did not obscure the view of those behind her. Two seats away from her — on the other side of

fashion's reigning monarch, Anna Wintour — was another of Her Majesty's sartorial secret weapons, Angela Kelly. The Scouser was the Queen's personal assistant. "Once she has chosen something to wear, I just want her to look good in it," Kelly once said.

Everything the Queen wore or carried was custom-made: she left the high street to the Duchess of Cambridge, and latterly the Duchess of Sussex, thank you very much. No playing the everywoman for her. She favoured a 2in block heel on her shoes (by Anello & Davide) to add height to her 5ft 4in stature without sacrificing comfort. Her

> 66
> At heart her choices were the regal equivalent of a hi-vis jacket

boxy patent bags (by Launer) were fitted with a longer than usual handle so they could be hooked over her forearm without catching on her cuff. A transparent Fulton umbrella — again, allowing her to be seen — was made to match each outfit. She was Queen of the drizzly British Isles, after all.

She had some more tricks up her sleeve too, or rather in her skirt: weights were fitted in every hemline. Why? I give you the assorted Marilyn Monroe moments of Kate's early years as duchess, when her skirt was blown upwards by the wind, risking the exposure of matters less than royal. »

1940s 1950s 1960s 1970s 1980s 1990s 2000s

As a young woman the Queen had the hourglass lines of another world-famous Elizabeth of the same era, Taylor, and worked them accordingly, although never inappropriately. That wasp waist and generous bosom were a perfect canvas for the bustier ball gowns that were once the bread and butter of state banquets and Disney films. As she grew older she came to favour sleek tailoring that skimmed rather than nipped in the waist.

Be it in her sylph years, or the stouter final decades, she never got it wrong. She approached getting dressed with the same

MEDIA DRUM IMAGES/IWM;
GETTY IMAGES; ALPHA PRESS; REX;
NATIONAL PICTURES; POPPERFOTO;
TIMES NEWSPAPERS LTD; INDIGO

sense of duty as she did being Queen. The same could not be said of her sister. As Princess Margaret aged she too thickened. Yet her fashion choices remained ill-advisedly extravagant. After a ball at Buckingham Palace in 1973 Cecil Beaton wrote with typical bite of the 43-year-old Margaret's "weighty body encased in sequin fargets, of turquoise and shrimp".

Fashion was not seen as a leveller by our monarch; quite the reverse. Take her 1947 wedding dress. What would be the embattled public's response to her extravagant seed-pearl-and-crystal-

encrusted Norman Hartnell confection? Not horror, as some feared, but delight at their twinkly fairytale princess amid all that drear. Besides, she had used clothing coupons, including an extra 200 provided by the government.

It was Hartnell she called on again to make her Coronation gown, insisting that the floral symbols of Great Britain and the Commonwealth be incorporated, from Irish shamrocks to Canadian maple leaves. Those shamrocks reappeared — 2,091 of them — embroidered on the dress she wore during her historic 2011 visit to Ireland. On royal

1940s   1950s   1960s   1970s   1980s   1990s   2000s

tours the Queen consistently used clothes to honour her host country.

How could anyone who wore a crown ignore the semiotics of dress? Indeed, so emblematic did the Queen's mode of attire become over the years that its influence could be seen on other women in the public eye, from Margaret Thatcher to Hillary Clinton (the former even co-opted those Launer handbags). We didn't recognise our Queen only from her head on our stamps, but from her signature ensembles, a fact that enabled the brilliant trompe l'oeil at the opening ceremony of the 2012 Olympics, in which the Queen appeared to parachute into the stadium in blush pink.

The young Elizabeth used Hartnell, her mother's favourite designer, during early adulthood. However, once she became Queen she worked with him to develop a different look, eschewing her mother's fussy chiffons in favour of sleeker lines. She was a woman in a man's world and she needed to dress to be taken seriously, while still signalling her femininity. She also came to rely on Hardy Amies, who was celebrated for his subtle re-toolings of Parisian trends; think couture with added stiff upper lip.

> **She had strong views on hats, above all, that she should wear one**

In more recent years the majority of the Queen's wardrobe was created by three in-house dressmakers and a milliner, with input from Kelly.

Away from the public eye the Queen didn't need any help getting dressed. She wore clothes that didn't get in the way of walking and riding, dogs and horses: tweed skirts, lace-up brown shoes, a headscarf, sensible woollies, assorted raincoats. The colours she chose were those of our country, her country: earth, moss, heather, lichen. She wore a kind of camouflage. In her private life she could, at last, blend in.

2010s

OUR LONGEST SERVING MONARCH

On April 29, 2011, Prince William married Catherine Middleton at Westminster Abbey. It was more than 63 years since Elizabeth and Philip had married there, and represented another step in ensuring that the line of succession would remain unbroken. Seven years later Prince Harry married the American actress Meghan Markle in a wedding at Windsor Castle that, for many, marked the royal family's arrival into a more multicultural age.

The Queen had for a long time been the most widely travelled head of state of all time. For political and other reasons, however, there were some places she had never visited. In May 2011 she made one of the most important state visits of her reign when she travelled to the Republic of Ireland for the first time. It was the result of highly delicate diplomatic manoeuvrings over many years, and was surrounded by much nervousness on both sides.

In the event it was a triumph. One of the most significant moments came on the first day, when she laid a wreath at the Garden of Remembrance in Dublin and bowed her head in recognition of those who had died fighting for Irish independence. The next evening a state dinner was held in her honour at Dublin Castle, in which the Queen gave a well-judged speech on relations between Britain and Ireland. She began with a few words in Irish, saying "A Uachtaráin, agus a chairde" — "President and friends" — at which the president, Mary McAleese, turned to others at the table and said: "Wow."

> **The marriage of Harry and Meghan marked the royal family's arrival into a more multicultural age**

For the Diamond Jubilee the next year the Queen and Philip confined their travels to the UK, while the rest of the family flew round the world on her behalf. The crowds that came out to see her during the jubilee celebrations were testament yet again to the affection and respect in which she was held. Standing on the balcony of Buckingham Palace as a sea of well-wishers filled The Mall all the way to Admiralty Arch, she said, "Oh my goodness, how extraordinary," as Prince William told her: "Those crowds are for you."

In a broadcast at the end of the celebrations she said it had all been "a humbling experience". It did not all pass off entirely smoothly, however. After a river pageant in which the royal couple stood on a barge enduring rain and cold winds, Philip was laid low by a bladder infection and went to hospital, missing the rest of the celebrations.

The Queen surpassed Victoria's record as the country's longest-reigning monarch on September 9, 2015. She had originally wanted the occasion to pass without fuss, but messages poured in from around the world and the crowds turned out as she carried out a day of engagements in Scotland.

Opening a railway station at Tweedbank, she said: "Inevitably a long life can pass by many milestones; my own is no exception. But I thank you all, and the many others at home and overseas, for your touching messages of great kindness."

Prince Philip, the man who had been by her side for nearly 70 years, retired from public duties in 2017. The Queen was slowing down too, handing over a number of her patronages to her children and grandchildren, and letting it be known that she would no longer undertake long-haul travel.

Meanwhile her family's capacity to make life difficult for her remained undiminished. In November 2019 the Duke of York gave a disastrous interview to BBC *Newsnight* about his friendship with Jeffrey Epstein, an American multimillionaire and convicted sex offender. The duke's explanations of his behaviour caused a furore and he was obliged to step back from his public duties.

And behind the scenes the Duke and Duchess of Sussex had another surprise in store.
Valentine Low

ALEXI LUBOMIRSKI/KENSINGTON PALACE

The royal family gather for an official portrait to mark the wedding of Prince Harry and Meghan Markle, May 2018 ❯❯

CHRIS JACKSON, CARL DE SOUZA, LEWIS WHYLD/AFP/GETTY IMAGES; DOMINIC LIPINSKI, PHIL NOBLE/PA

LEFT
On Her Majesty's secret service: James Bond (Daniel Craig) and Paul Whybrew, page of the backstairs, escort the Queen to a helicopter for the opening ceremony of the London 2012 Olympics. The Queen demanded a speaking part in the sequence directed by Danny Boyle, in which a stunt double parachuted into the stadium

RIGHT
Barack Obama beams at the Queen during a state banquet at Buckingham Palace in 2011. The US president and his wife, Michelle, developed a firm bond with the Queen, and in 2016 attended a special lunch at Windsor Castle to celebrate her 90th birthday

The royal family gather with dignitaries from all over the world at Westminster Abbey for the wedding of Prince William and Catherine Middleton, April 29, 2011

LEFT
The mother of the bride, Carole Middleton, the Queen and the Duchess of Cornwall after the service

RIGHT
One is very amused! From top: a moment of mirth with the Duchess of Cambridge at a children's sports event in Nottingham in 2012; Her Majesty and Prince Charles are tickled by the tug of war and other Highland games at the Braemar Gathering in 2010 »

The Queen and Prince Philip walk through a carpet of 888,246 ceramic poppies, one for each British or colonial serviceman killed in the First World War, at the Tower of London. The installation commemorated the 2014 centenary of the outbreak of the war

ABOVE
The royal barge Gloriana carried the Queen and Prince Philip past Westminster on the River Thames as part of the 670-boat Diamond Jubilee flotilla in June 2012

ABOVE
The Queen with the Irish president Michael D Higgins in the Green Drawing Room at Windsor Castle in 2014. It was the first state visit to the UK by an Irish head of state

ABOVE
Travelling in the horse-drawn Irish state coach, the Queen and Prince Philip return from the state opening of parliament in 2015 »

RIGHT
Her Majesty arrives at King's Lynn train station in Norfolk in 2018 to begin her annual Christmas holiday at Sandringham. The Queen and Prince Philip regularly took scheduled trains for this annual trip, paying for off-peak first class singles from King's Cross — with the one concession being a whole carriage reserved for the royal party

ABOVE
With John Warren, her racing manager, and Princess Michael of Kent, the Queen watches the Derby Day racing from the royal box at Epsom racecourse on June 6, 2015

LEFT
At London Fashion Week in 2018 with Anna Wintour, the editor of Vogue (second from right), and the royal dressmaker Angela Kelly, the Queen's long-time confidante (far right)

To her eight grandchildren, she was simply 'Granny'

The Queen had to juggle motherhood with the demands of being a new monarch, so it is little wonder that she relished being a grandparent, writes the Times feature writer Damian Whitworth

To the world she was the Queen, but to her eight grandchildren she was simply "Granny". Prince William once explained the reality of growing up as a grandson of the most famous woman in the world: "She's my grandmother to me first and then she's the Queen."

This was demonstrated most clearly after the death of his mother, Diana, Princess of Wales, in 1997. The Queen was criticised for a perceived failure to respond to the public mood when she did not return from Balmoral to London, where large crowds were mourning.

On this occasion, however, her instincts as a grandmother trumped her sense of duty as Queen. Her first priority was to stay with William and Harry in Scotland and help them to grieve in private.

Years later, when Harry announced that he wished to retreat from royal life with his family, she had to be firm about the terms of the separation. She had to be a queen first and a grandmother second.

As boys, the princes formed a strong bond with their grandmother. Most weekends during their years at Eton College they would walk across the river to spend time at Windsor Castle with the Queen.

In an interview at the time of the Diamond Jubilee, Harry said: "To me she's just 'Granny'." He and his brother shouted, "Go Granny!" during the opening ceremony of the London Olympics in 2012 when a stunt appeared to show Her Majesty parachuting out of a helicopter with Daniel Craig's James Bond.

In 2016 Harry and his grandmother collaborated on a humorous video to promote the Invictus Games, the competition for wounded service personnel that he created. President Obama and his wife, Michelle, appeared, challenging Harry

over his invitation to "bring it" at the games. When a US serviceman said "boom" and made a drop-the-mike gesture, the Queen said, "Oh really, please," and exchanged pitying smiles with her grandson.

After his wedding in 2011 William offered an insight into how the Queen could cut through royal pomp to ensure that he and his intended bride were not swamped by tradition. Once William had announced his engagement to Kate Middleton, Palace bureaucracy swung into action on a scale that alarmed the prince.

"I was given this official list of 777 names — dignitaries, governors, all sorts of people — and not one person I knew," he recalled. "They said, 'These are the people we should invite.' I looked at it in absolute horror and said, 'I think we should start again.' I rang her up the next day and said, 'Do we need to be doing this?' And she said, 'No. Start with your friends first and then go from there.' And she told me to bin the list. She made the point that there are certain times when you have to strike the right balance."

The Queen's grandchildren are William and Harry; Princess Beatrice and Princess Eugenie, the children of the Duke of York;

> ## "
> When you get a letter from her or a bit of praise, it goes a long, long way
>
> Prince William, 2011

BELOW
The Queen and Prince Harry in the video promoting the 2016 Invictus Games

Peter Phillips and Zara Tindall, the children of the Princess Royal; Lady Louise Windsor and James, Viscount Severn, the children of the Earl of Wessex. Her 12 great-grandchildren are: Prince George, Princess Charlotte and Prince Louis of Wales, Savannah and Isla Phillips, Mia, Lena and Lucas Tindall, Archie and Lilibet Mountbatten-Windsor, August Brooksbank and Sienna Mapelli Mozzi. When George was a toddler, his mother disclosed, he called the Queen "Gan-Gan".

The Queen greatly enjoyed her annual pre-Christmas lunches at Buckingham Palace, which were an opportunity to get as many members of the extended family together as possible. She had the sort of warm relationships that the Queen Mother had with her great-grandchildren. (The Queen Mother once reduced them to giggles with an impression of Ali G.)

The Duke of York once suggested that the Queen had been more comfortable as a grandmother than she had been as a mother, which was hardly surprising, given

that she was a young woman when she had to juggle motherhood with monarchy.

Eugenie, now a director at an art gallery and married to Jack Brooksbank, once said her grandmother "lights up" around her grandchildren. She would take them raspberry picking when they were young and listened to Eugenie's stories of life at Newcastle University when she was a student, taking an interest in her essays.

The Queen was very close to the children of her youngest son, the Earl of Wessex, who decided against giving them the titles of Prince and Princess. The family live at Bagshot Park, a short drive from Windsor, and the children would often go riding with their grandmother.

As a young girl Lady Louise bore a striking resemblance to her grandmother at the same age, and spent time talking horses with the Queen at the Royal Mews at Windsor, where her pony is stabled.

The Queen liked nothing more than to attend events where she had a role as a grandmother and a queen. At Harry's

ABOVE
The Queen with her grandchildren James, Viscount Severn, left, and Lady Louise Windsor, in Windsor Great Park, 2011

RIGHT
With Zara Phillips on Gold Cup day at the Cheltenham festival, 2003

passing out parade at the Royal Military Academy Sandhurst in 2006 she made her grandson smile as she inspected the solemn-faced new officers. William said that with her family she liked to laugh about things that had gone wrong at formal events. "The Queen has seen so many parades or performances when there's a small slip-up it tickles her humour."

He also said that for a grandson who will one day sit on the throne, she was a constant source of inspiration and wise counsel. "There is no question that you can ask, and no point you can raise that she won't already know about — and have a better opinion about," he told the author Robert Hardman, for his book *Our Queen*. "She's very up for that sort of thing.

"And for me particularly, being the young bloke coming through, being able to talk to my grandmother, ask her questions and know that there's sound advice coming back is very reassuring."

After going to see victims of the Australian floods and New Zealand earthquake in 2011, William received a note from the Queen congratulating him on the way he represented her. "When you get a letter from her or a bit of praise, it goes a long, long way, more so than anyone else saying 'well done' to you. It's mainly because there's such gravitas behind those words."

Like all grandparents she saw her grandchildren make mistakes, but their indiscretions were often splashed across newspapers: Prince Harry in a Nazi uniform, smoking cannabis or playing strip poker; his rather better-behaved brother, William, photographed partying hard in nightclubs, or landing his helicopter in the back garden of his girlfriend's parents' home.

As the grandchildren grew up, it seemed she would have less reason to worry about bad headlines, even if her pride in William and Harry's military service must have been tempered by concern, especially when Harry was in Afghanistan. She was always keen to hear about their charity commitments.

One of the few occasions when Buckingham Palace made it clear that the monarch disapproved of a grandchild's behaviour was when Peter Phillips sold the photos of his wedding at Windsor Castle to *Hello!* There were raised eyebrows when his sister, Zara, and her husband, Mike Tindall, appeared in the same magazine with their baby daughter, Mia.

Then came news of the painful rift between William and Harry and the

decision in 2020 of the Sussexes to step back from the family and build a privately funded life on the other side of the Atlantic. The timing of the Sussexes' announcement of the move, before a deal had been worked out, caused uproar and must have been painful for the Queen, who was 93.

She had to be tough. She could not be an indulgent granny and accept Harry's vague ambitions to remain half in the family, performing some royal duties while making his own money. For the sake of the monarchy, she had to insist on a much cleaner severing of ties. Nevertheless, Harry and his grandmother shared a Sunday lunch alone together in March 2020, in her apartment at Windsor Castle, shortly before he and his wife's final royal public appearance. The Queen made it clear she would always support him, and he would always be welcomed back. Then when Harry and Meghan gave their

interview to Oprah Winfrey, the Queen found herself, at 94, dealing with one of the most serious crises of her reign. Meghan spoke in the interview of feeling suicidal and not being helped by "the institution" and of unnamed members of the family expressing concerns about "how dark" Archie's skin would be, while Harry said that he and the rest of the royal family were "trapped".

The statement issued in response on behalf of the Queen said that the issues raised by the interview were concerning and were taken very seriously but that "some recollections may vary". Harry, Meghan and Archie would "always be much-loved family members".

Harry said in the interview that he had Zoom calls with his grandmother to show her Archie and insisted: "I've spoken more to my grandmother in the last year than I have done for many, many years." He added: "My grandmother and I have a really good relationship... and an understanding. And I have a deep respect for her. She's my colonel-in-chief, right? She always will be."

2020s

THE LOSS OF HER 'STRENGTH AND STAY'

If the Queen had been nurturing any ideas that the last years of her reign would be a peaceful time, when her family united in support of an ageing monarch, she would have been sadly mistaken. In January 2020, frustrated at their inability to carve out a new role for themselves, the Duke and Duchess of Sussex announced they were stepping back as "senior members" of the royal family. That the couple were unhappy and wanted out was not news to the royal family, but what came as a shock was that they were prepared to release a statement with just a few minutes' warning. The Queen was said to be "disappointed".

She also turned out to be a tough negotiator; Harry and Meghan were forced to relinquish their royal roles completely, and went off to California to forge a new life funded by Netflix and Spotify. In March 2021 they spoke to the US television chat show host Oprah Winfrey, making pointed claims about the royal family's treatment of Meghan. The claims caused a stir, but the UK now had other concerns. No sooner had the couple left than the country was gripped by the coronavirus outbreak. In a rare broadcast to the nation, the Queen said Britain would "succeed" in its fight against the

> ## For the Queen, Covid restrictions brought one benefit. Prince Philip came to join her bubble at Windsor Castle

pandemic, and that eventually better times would return. In an echo of the wartime Vera Lynn hit, she told people: "We will meet again."

For the Queen, Covid restrictions brought at least one benefit. Prince Philip, who had been spending much of his retirement at Wood Farm on the Sandringham estate, came to join her in her coronavirus bubble at Windsor Castle, where she enjoyed the renewed pleasure of having lunch with her husband every day.

Philip died at Windsor Castle on April 9, 2021, just over two months before what would have been his 100th birthday. They had been married for 73 years. At his funeral, a pared-down service at St George's Chapel, Windsor, the Queen cut a lonely figure, all in black and wearing a mask. A wreath was placed on top of Philip's coffin with a handwritten card from the Queen, which said simply: "In loving memory". The card was said to have been signed with her nickname from childhood, "Lilibet".

Then trouble with the Duke of York stirred again as a US court case loomed in which Virginia Giuffre claimed she had been trafficked to have sex with the duke. He denied the claims — then settled out of court for millions.

For all the turmoil, the Queen showed remarkable stoicism. She caught Covid at 95, recovered and resumed her duties. Her public appearances grew infrequent but she never lost her ability to surprise: during her Platinum Jubilee she appeared in a film with Paddington Bear, producing a marmalade sandwich from her handbag. Just 48 hours before her death at the age of 96 she installed Liz Truss as her 15th prime minister. It was a life devoted to service, in all its forms.
Valentine Low

RIGHT
With the country under lockdown during the Covid pandemic in April 2020, the Queen's message of hope is displayed on advertising boards at an eerily deserted Piccadilly Circus in central London »

NEIL HALL/EPA

" We should take comfort that while we may have more still to endure, better days will return "

Her Majesty The Queen
Message to the Nation

Photo: PA Media

ABOVE
The Queen rides Balmoral Fern, one of her fell ponies, in Windsor Home Park, May 2020

TOP RIGHT
The Queen and the Duke of Edinburgh released this image of them at Windsor Castle to mark his 99th birthday on June 10, 2020, during the first Covid lockdown

RIGHT
The Queen and Prince Philip open a card made by Prince George, Princess Charlotte and Prince Louis on the occasion of their 73rd wedding anniversary, November 20, 2020

The Duke of Edinburgh died on April 9, 2021, aged 99. His coffin was conveyed to his funeral at St George's Chapel at Windsor Castle by a Land Rover that he had helped to design for the occasion

BELOW
Observing Covid restrictions, the monarch sits alone in St George's Chapel for the funeral of Prince Philip, her husband of 73 years, on April 17, 2021 »

LEFT, TOP
The Queen embraces the digital age during the Covid pandemic by holding a virtual audience with the Hungarian ambassador, Ferenc Kumin, and his wife in December 2020

ABOVE
Her Majesty smiles as she drives from Windsor Castle to the Royal Windsor Horse Show, July 2021

LEFT
The centenarian fundraiser Captain Tom Moore is knighted in a special ceremony at Windsor Castle, July 2020

RIGHT, TOP
Marmalade sandwich, Ma'am? Paddington pops round for tea to kick off the Platinum Jubilee party in June 2022

RIGHT, BOTTOM
The Queen prepares to appoint Liz Truss as prime minister at Balmoral on September 6, 2022. She died two days later

It was all about The Queue

About 250,000 people queued to see the Queen lying in state, some waiting for more than 24 hours. The Times columnist Caitlin Moran reflects on the powerful emotional aftermath of the Queen's death

Were you there for Beckham? Or the man who touched the plinth? Or the man who left the mysterious note on the plinth? Or the Royal Archer — poor old dude — who fainted? Or the man who "rushed" the plinth, and got as far as "disrupting the flag" before he was apprehended by security? Not that we actually got to see that — the BBC's 24/7 live coverage, on a five-second delay, managed to replace the broadcast with its stock, calming photo of Big Ben, accompanied by the soothing sound of a babbling brook. We all knew something had happened — they don't bring out that shot of Big Ben for nothing — but had to rely on the next day's tabloids for the full story. The BBC doesn't do the... distasteful moments.

But then, in many ways, these very infrequent moments of drama were not the most fascinating thing about The Queue — that phenomenon that dominated the news, as the Queen lay in state at Westminster Hall, and we lived in the odd, in-between, limbo days from the announcement of the Queen's death, on September 8, to her funeral, 11 days later.

No, the real drama was the hundreds of thousands of people, from every corner of the country, filing past the Queen's coffin in a perfectly orderly manner. All on best behaviour — red-eyed, footsore and utterly determined to be there. Some reverent, some in tears, some covered in medals and crisply saluting, some mouthing "goodbye". The young man in shades, chewing gum, who tried to Fonz his way through the whole experience — despite having queued 14 hours to show his wildly contradictory insouciance. The odd ex-hippy in yoga pants throwing in a "namaste", before presumably going to do some sun salutations on Westminster Green. I was captivated by all of them. Every single person, all 250,000 of them, as they paused in front of the coffin, was like a tiny, three-second play. A single stitch in the Bayeux of mourning. I wanted to watch every single one. And I pretty much did.

I think our fascination with The Queue was because, even though the Queen had died, the velocity of interest in her remained, not even the same, but radically heightened. And, in the absence of her being able to do anything any more — there were no more appearances, parades, garden parties, bright hats or carefully worded speeches — all the still-galloping interest in her transmuted, instantly, like magic, into an obsession with The Queue. As Emma Thompson once noted in an interview, when you're playing a queen, the way the audience knows you're a queen is the way everyone else reacts around them. They bow, they tremble, they become, temporarily, someone else. Someone in the presence of power.

The Queue, then, was one of the final scenes in the Queen's life — where we saw her power in this final reaction shot from her subjects. It was how she manifested in our heads, suddenly made flesh — five miles long, drawn from every demographic and corner of the country, and visible from planes circling to land at Heathrow. Finally, you could see how we felt about being people who are born with a Queen as part of their money, stamps, Christmas, public holidays and lives.

So as we look back, let us ask that most perennial of questions: did we understand what all this was really about? What does all of this tell us about Britain?

Britain cannot helping being 100 per cent Britain, 100 per cent of the time

The fact that Britain has responded to a period of immense cultural upheaval by producing a series of gigantic queues has been viewed, by the rest of the world, as absolutely adorable. The Brits are — queueing! Doing our most stereotypical national thing, spontaneously, and on a grand scale! I guess it's like if the death of Macron were greeted by the French having multiple affairs in front of the Sacré Coeur; or the Australians coped with the death of Paul "Crocodile Dundee" Hogan by barbecuing the world's biggest sausage. We've been so endearingly us.

And our geography has helped us: these queues have taken places outside Tower Bridge, the Tower of London, Shakespeare's Globe, the National Theatre, the London Eye, Lambeth Palace, the Houses of Parliament and Windsor Castle. Pretty much all of our best-known landmarks. Unless the The Queue had also snaked past Hugh Grant stuttering, "In the words of the Partridge family, I think I love you!" and Adele drinking a pint, we couldn't have done better.

Contrary to how watching the BBC's 24/7 live coverage made you feel, everyone in Britain was not in The Queue

On Sunday I decided I had to act on my obsession, and went down to Westminster Hall to see what it was all actually like. As a representative of *The Times*, I was able to join the international press pack and stand in the press enclosure in Westminster Hall: an experience that was both an immense privilege I do not in any way underestimate, but also turned out to be exactly as it looks on the television.

After 45 minutes I went outside, to experience The Queue in the flesh. It was an immensely British experience — thousands of volunteers lined the route, cheering the Queuers on, as if this were the slowest London Marathon ever. One sat on a chair, wielding an immense bucket and

> **Every single person was a stitch in the Bayeux of mourning**

where the snow globe of life is shaken up and normal life is hidden in a temporary flurry. Much of Britain, I think, quietly enjoyed this holiday from normality.

So much of all this was about women
Anyone who saw the TV footage would have noticed that The Queue was massively dominated by women: women in groups of friends, women who had come down with their mothers, or daughters; women who had travelled alone, but made lifelong friends within hours.

This does sound foolish, and stupid, but it wasn't until I watched Channel 4's *Andrew Neil: Britain After the Queen*, and heard Joan Bakewell talking, that I realised something very obvious, and very important — just how extraordinary it was that, for a long time, one of the most important people in the world was a woman. Bakewell pointed out what a disruption it was to the normal order of things when, in 1952, a very young woman became our Queen. Suddenly, this girl, in her dresses and lipstick, took her place at the global top table, upturning the natural look and order of power.

Young women always look like the future, I think: especially back in the 20th century, when having the vote still seemed fresh, and we had not yet had Women's Liberation, or any waves of feminism. Having only ever known a world where one of the most powerful people in it was a woman, able to make even someone as egotistical and bombastic as Donald Trump become momentarily overawed and attempt propriety, has lowered our national blood pressure at a very primal level.

This is why the image that stayed with me — seen over and over in Westminster Hall — was the innumerable women who, for their moment in front of the Queen's coffin, did something I have never seen before during a lying in state. I do not know which woman was the first to do it, but after her, thousands did it, over and over, in her wake. On reaching their moment, at the end of The Queue — some having waited up to 24 hours, often with very small children — they blew a kiss to the Queen, and mouthed "thank you" before smiling and then bursting into tears.

In that moment, there was no subject or monarch; no status divide at all. There was just a woman, saying goodbye to another woman, who they felt — like all women, and mothers, and grandmothers — really had tried her best. And now they were saying goodbye.

---

shouting: "Werther's Original? Go on — help yourself! You deserve it."

And the main thing I noticed about The Queue in the flesh is that most people around The Queue were not in The Queue. The ratio seemed to be "20 per cent people in The Queue" to "80 per cent people who've come to see The Queue" — or just experience the general upside down, rules suspension of the whole thing. On Westminster Bridge a group of women — from Malaysia, I think — were holding a fashion show: using the bridge as a catwalk while filming a series of outfit changes, backdropped by Big Ben, for what I presume was their YouTube channel. Next to them, the indefatigable crank Piers Corbyn was handing out leaflets warning against the

Covid vaccine; a group of teenagers, presumably all vaccinated, were turning them into paper planes and joyfully flying them across the Thames.

This is the part that has, I think, been underreported, for fear of coming across as disrespectful, or inappropriate: how much this odd time has come as an unexpected but very welcome disruption to the normal course of things. Like a wet playtime at school: there was suddenly a bank holiday, and Prince Charles being angry with a pen, and Liz Truss's weird curtsy, and horses wearing feathery hats, and something to talk about, for a brief time at least, that isn't politics, or gas bills or the war.

A death is, yes, about grieving, and reflection — but it is also the moment

ABOVE

The queue, which was ten miles at its longest, stretched past London landmarks such as Tower Bridge

LEFT
The Queen's eight grandchildren holding their vigil in Westminster Hall on the Saturday of the lying in state

SPLASH NEWS; YUI MOK/PA

Carried to her rest

The Queen was buried at Windsor after tens of thousands lined the streets for a funeral marked by splendour and pageantry, writes Valentine Low, the Times royal correspondent

It was the longest of farewells, a day of history marked with tears and marching bands, timeless ceremony and an outpouring of emotion during which tens of thousands lined the streets to catch their last glimpse of the Queen.

It began with the splendour of a state funeral at Westminster Abbey, where world leaders gathered to pay respect to the monarch who had acceded to the throne before most of them were born. It ended eight hours later when, in an intimate ceremony away from the cameras, her family saw her buried alongside the Duke of Edinburgh in a crypt at St George's Chapel, Windsor.

A day that had been planned for decades began with the Queen's coffin being taken from Westminster Hall, where she lay in state for four days, to the abbey, borne on a gun carriage drawn by 142 naval ratings.

The coffin was draped with the royal standard and topped with the instruments of state: the imperial state crown, the orb and the sceptre. Next to them sat a wreath of flowers picked from the gardens at Buckingham Palace, Clarence House and Highgrove. Tucked among the flowers was a handwritten message from the King, which said: "In loving and devoted memory. Charles R."

The coffin was followed on foot by the King and other royal family members, including his sons the Prince of Wales and Duke of Sussex. Inside the abbey they were joined by the two youngest members of the royal family ever to join a royal funeral procession, Prince George, nine, and Princess Charlotte, seven.

At the funeral service more than 2,000 mourners filled the abbey, including some 200 heads of state, foreign royals and other overseas dignitaries. Most were bussed to the abbey. President Biden of the US was one of the few granted permission to take his own transport.

They were joined by emergency workers, members of the late Queen's household and holders of the George Cross and Victoria Cross. In the abbey David Hoyle, the dean of Westminster, spoke of the Queen's sense of duty and "her long life of selfless service". He said: "With gratitude we remember her unswerving commitment to a high calling over so many years as Queen and head of the Commonwealth. With admiration we recall her lifelong sense of duty and dedication to her people."

The Archbishop of Canterbury said she had touched "a multitude" of lives in her 70-year reign.

The service ended with the Last Post and two minutes' silence before the sovereign's piper played a lament. Then, carried by a bearer party from the Queen's Company, 1st Battalion Grenadier Guards, the coffin was moved out to the gun carriage to be taken in procession to Wellington Arch.

The security challenge of hosting so many of the world's VIPs meant that the area around Westminster Abbey was completely closed to the public. Instead the crowds, which had been gathering for days in the hope of a glimpse of the procession, lined Whitehall, The Mall and Hyde Park Corner.

As the King and other royals followed on foot, their faces stoical, some members of the public were in tears. They were mourning the only monarch most of them had known. The procession was led by Royal Canadian Mounties followed by NHS workers including May Parsons, who administered the first Covid-19 vaccine in 2020. The procession was formed of seven groups and made its way around Parliament Square, past a guard of honour comprising army, navy and RAF personnel. In total, more than 3,000 members of the military took part. ➤ Continued on page 134

> **After a two minute silence the Queen's piper played a lament**

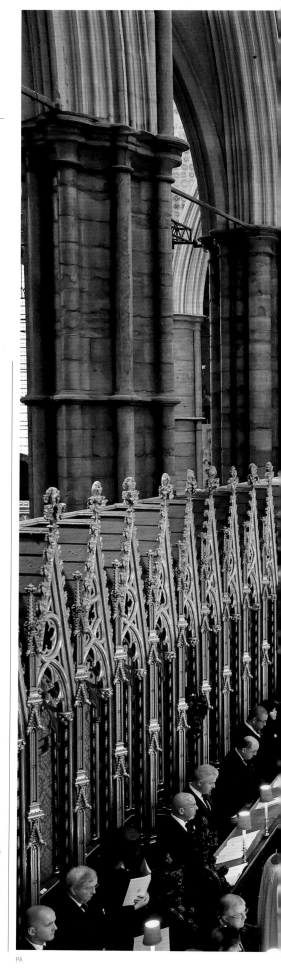

RIGHT
The Queen's coffin is carried into Westminster Abbey; her eight pallbearers, from the Queen's Company, 1st Battalion Grenadier Guards, had been flown back from Iraq to take part in the funeral

PA

ABOVE
The gun carriage carrying the Queen's coffin to the abbey was first used for Queen Victoria's funeral; it is pulled by 142 naval ratings

LEFT
Camilla, the Queen Consort, the Duchess of Sussex, Prince George, the Princess of Wales, Princess Charlotte and the Countess of Wessex outside the abbey

RIGHT
King Charles leads members of the royal family in procession as the Queen's coffin is carried from the abbey

ABOVE
The procession after the service moves down The Mall towards Buckingham Palace

LEFT
At Wellington Arch, the coffin is transferred to a hearse for the journey to Windsor

RIGHT
Prince William and Prince Harry walking behind the Queen's coffin

At Wellington Arch the coffin was transferred to the state hearse to be driven to Windsor for the committal service at St George's Chapel. By the time it reached the Long Walk, where thousands more had gathered, the hearse was strewn with flowers thrown by mourners.

As the procession made its way through Windsor Great Park, Terry Pendry, the Queen's head groom, led out Emma, her fell pony, to see the coffin go past. At Windsor Castle, where the royal family once more formed a procession behind the hearse, there was another poignant moment when two of the Queen's corgis, Muick and Sandy, were brought out.

At the committal service the final ceremony marking the death of the sovereign took place. The instruments of state were removed from the coffin and placed on the altar. The lord chamberlain broke his wand of office, which was placed on the coffin along with the camp colour of the Queen's Company, 1st Battalion Grenadier Guards, to be buried with her.

Then, as David Conner, the dean of Windsor, proclaimed the words, "Go forth upon thy journey from this world, O Christian soul", the coffin was lowered into the royal vault. The service ended with the Garter King of Arms reading the styles and titles of Queen Elizabeth II, a blessing and

> ## By the time the hearse reached Windsor it was strewn with flowers

the singing of the national anthem. With that, a long day of public ceremonial was over. But for the royal family, there was one last chance to say their farewells. At 7.30pm, after the coffins of the Queen and the Duke of Edinburgh had been brought up from the royal vault, a private burial ceremony was held in the King George VI Memorial Chapel. There the Queen and her husband were buried together, alongside her parents, George VI and Queen Elizabeth the Queen Mother, and her sister, Princess Margaret.

The grave is marked with a slab of black marble that is already inscribed with her parents' names. It will now also bear the words: Elizabeth II 1926-2022.

INTRODUCTION TO
ASTRONOMY

INTRODUCTION TO
ASTRONOMY

IAN RIDPATH

TODTRI

PICTURE CREDITS

All pictures supplied by **Galaxy Picture Library** except for the following:

Christie's Images: 17

This book was designed and produced by
TODTRI Book Publishers
P.O. Box 572, New York, NY 10116-0572
Fax: (212) 695-6984
e-mail: todtri@mindspring.com

Printed and bound in Singapore

ISBN 1-57717-160-8

Visit us on the web!
www.todtri.com

Author: Ian Ridpath

Publisher: Robert M. Tod
Editor: Nicolas Wright
Captions researched and written by John Richardson
Art Director: Ron Pickless
Typesetting & DTP: Blanc Verso UK

CONTENTS

THE UNIVERSE & THE BIG BANG

Opposite: A total Solar Eclipse seen from India in 1995. The large "cloud" seen beyond the edge of the shadow is called the Corona.

Below: A weather satellite image of the Western Hemisphere.

News travels fast in the Universe – in fact, at the speed of light, 186,000 miles (300,000 kilometres) per second, the fastest speed known. Even so, our "live" view of the heavens is not as up-to-date as we might think, and the news from the cosmos becomes increasingly old the farther off we look. This is because, as any traveller knows, distance and time are inextricably linked, so when we look out into the Universe, we are also looking back in time.

To get an idea of the scale of the Universe, let's step away from our home planet, the Earth, and into space, beginning with the Moon, our closest celestial neighbour, a mere 239,000 miles (384,400 km) away. Light (and radio waves, which travel at the same speed) cross that distance in just over a second. Spacecraft from Earth take a couple of days for the same journey.

Light from the Sun, our parent star, takes 8.3 minutes to reach us, across a distance of 93 million miles (150 million km). So, if anything happened on the Sun one morning, we would have time to finish breakfast before the news arrived.

From the outermost planet of our Solar System, Pluto, 30 times farther from the Sun than we are, light takes over four hours to arrive. A space probe would take several years to travel that far.

Beyond the edge of the Solar System, there is a gulf before we come to the stars. Nearest to the Sun is Alpha Centauri (actually not one star but three), light from which takes over four years to reach us. Our fastest space probes would take the best part of 100,000 years to reach Alpha Centauri, a clear indication that interstellar travel will not be possible with current technology.

Stars, which are self-luminous spheres of gas, club together in huge aggregations termed galaxies. The nearest major galaxy, in Andromeda, appears as it was over two million years in the past, while the most distant reaches of the Universe, accessible

only to large telescopes, are seen as they were billions of years ago, before the Earth was born.

So unimaginably vast are the distances in the Universe that astronomers abandon Earthbound measures such as miles and kilometres in favour of a unit based on the travel time of light – the light year. This, the distance covered by a light beam in a year, is equivalent to 5.9 million million miles (9.5 million million km). By this reckoning, Alpha Centauri is just over four light years away, the Andromeda galaxy about 2.5 million light years away, and so on.

OUR GALAXY

Our Sun is an average star, one of at least 100 billion stars that make up our Galaxy – written with a capital G, to distinguish it from other galaxies. The Galaxy is shaped like a Catherine-wheel spiral, roughly 100,000 light years wide. In this stellar city our Sun is a suburban resident, situated about two-thirds the way to the rim.

With a stately grace befitting its huge girth, our Galaxy slowly turns on its axis, although not as a solid wheel. Each star follows its own orbit around the Galaxy's hub under the same laws of gravity that govern the motion of satellites, moons, and planets. Our Sun takes more than 200 million years to complete one circuit of the Galaxy

Above: A view of the United States taken by a weather satellite at night. This image shows what astronomers call "light pollution". This can be real problem when making observations of faint objects. Light pollution comes mainly from street lights.

Left: The Milky Way as seen in the constellation of Sagittarius. The view of the Milky Way is especially good in this direction as it looks towards the hub of our Galaxy.

Previous pages: Star Trails over the Gemini 8-m telescope. On the left is the glow from Kilauea Volcano. This picture was taken with a long exposure time. The arcs in the sky are caused by the movement of the earth when the shutter of the camera was open. The two bands of light by the bottom of the telescope were caused by a car's headlights.

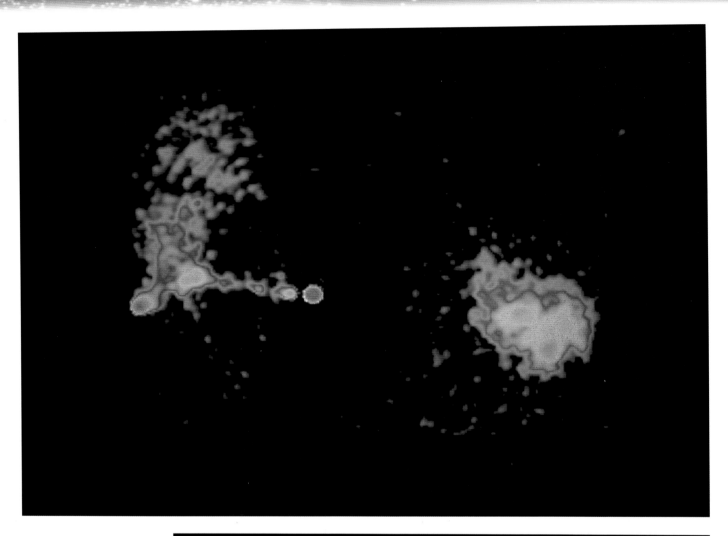

Above: A false colour image of Quasar 3C179 with radio lobes. These jets of red hot matter stream out from the centre of the Quasar at right angles to the accretion disk.

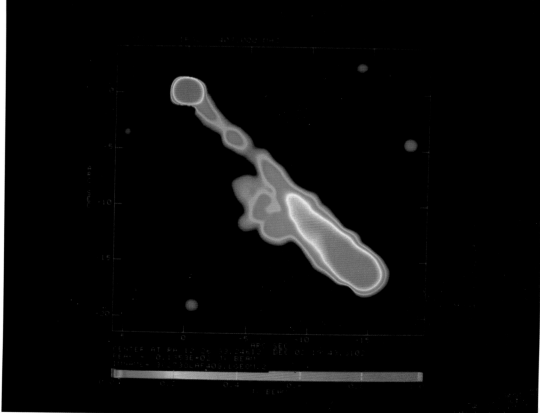

Right: The Quasar 3C273. This false colour image of the quasar shows the distribution of matter within the galaxy.

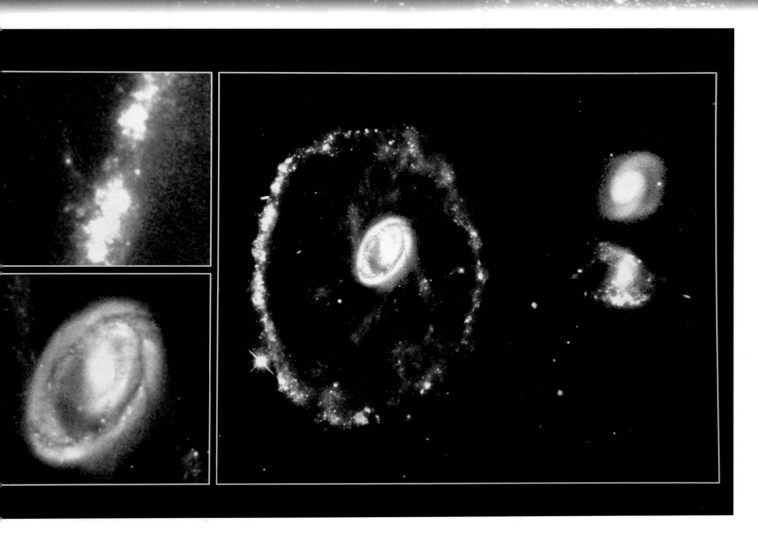

supergiants with ten times the number of stars in our Galaxy. Such galaxies are predatory, having grown to their present bloated size by swallowing smaller passers-by.

MYSTERIES OF DEEP SPACE

Certain galaxies are hyperactive. The first examples, spiral galaxies with unusually bright centres, were found in 1943 by the American astronomer Carl K. Seyfert, after whom they are named. At their brilliant cores, Seyfert galaxies appear to have a ring of hot, glowing gas, termed an accretion disk, whirling around an unseen central mass.

Subsequently, galaxies were found that emit powerful radio waves, not just from their cores but also from huge jets and clouds that extend for millions of light years on either side. Radio galaxies are usually giant ellipticals, and their violent activity most likely results from immense traffic accidents, as they collide and merge with smaller galaxies.

The most extreme activity occurs in objects termed quasars, so named from their quasi-stellar appearance when first photographed in the 1960s. Quasars are extremely distant and super-powerful, emitting as much light as many galaxies like our own. Yet all this energy comes from a region far smaller than the distance between the Sun and Alpha Centauri.

In all such cases of hyperactivity, the central power sources are thought to be monster black holes containing as much matter as a billion Suns. The black hole's mighty gravitational grip shreds stars into gas like a kitchen blender, swirling the gas around in the accretion disk and heating it to millions of degrees before swallowing it. Not all the gas goes down the hatch, though; some is belched out along the black hole's rotation axis, at right angles to the accretion disk, forming the long streamers that we see flanking radio galaxies.

One reason why quasars shine so brightly is that the black holes at their centres have a copious supply of gas. Pictures

Above: The unusual looking Cartwheel Galaxy, 500 million light years away in the constellation Sculptor, has a yellowish hub and a blue rim, seen through the Hubble Space Telescope. Its strange shape is thought to have arisen when the small galaxy at upper right passed through it about 200 million years ago.

from the Hubble Space Telescope show that in many cases quasar activity occurs where galaxies are colliding and merging, pouring new fuel into the black-hole furnace. The black hole continues to grow until it runs out of stars and gas to cannibalize, then the quasar activity switches off. Similar activity, on a smaller scale, may be a feature of all galactic nuclei at some stage in their lives.

THE EXPANDING UNIVERSE

The Universe consists of everything that exists – all matter, energy, space and time. Cosmology is the name given to the study of the origin and evolution of the Universe. It is an immense undertaking, which has produced remarkable results in recent years.

First, though, we must go back to 1929 when the key to modern cosmology was cut by the American astronomer Edwin Hubble. Observing with the 100-inch (2.5-m) telescope on Mount Wilson, California, he found that distant galaxies were receding from us at high speed. What's more, their speeds increased with their distance, as though the entire Universe were expanding like a balloon being pumped up.

Galaxies show no change in position over many human lifetimes, so how could Hubble tell that they were receding and what their speeds were? He did so by analysing their light with a device called a spectroscope, which spreads light into its constituent colours. Light from the galaxies showed a displacement towards to the red end of the spectrum, termed a redshift. This is analogous to the drop in pitch of a sound from a passing vehicle, which we know as the Doppler effect. Like the drop in pitch of sound, the reddening of light is caused by a stretching of wavelength as the source moves away, and it becomes more marked with the object's speed.

Hubble's discovery of the expansion of the Universe, coupled with paper calculations by theoreticians, gave rise to the idea that the Universe was created billions of years ago in an immense fireball – the Big Bang. Its basic premise is easily understood: if the Universe is expanding, every-

thing within it must have been much closer together in the past. Turn the clock back far enough, and you reach a time when everything in the Universe was squeezed together in a superdense, superhot ball, which began its explosive expansion in the Big Bang.

What's less easy to understand is that the galaxies are not rushing outwards into preexisting empty space. Actually, it is space itself that is expanding, carrying the galaxies with it like flotsam on an ebb tide. Since the speed at which objects move apart increases with their separation, the redshift of galaxies and quasars is a guide to their distance from us.

ECHOES OF THE BIG BANG

Obtaining direct observational evidence that the Big Bang actually occurred might seem impossible, but in 1965 two American radio engineers at Bell Telephone Laboratories in New Jersey,

Above: Astronomers contemplating the universe by Bartholomaeus Anglicus Nevers or Bourges c.1472.

Opposite: The Andromeda galaxy was mentioned as early as AD 965, in the *Book of the Fixed Stars*, by the Islamic astronomer al-Sufi, and rediscovered in 1612, by the German astronomer Simon Marius, who said 'it resembled the light of a candle seen through a horn'.

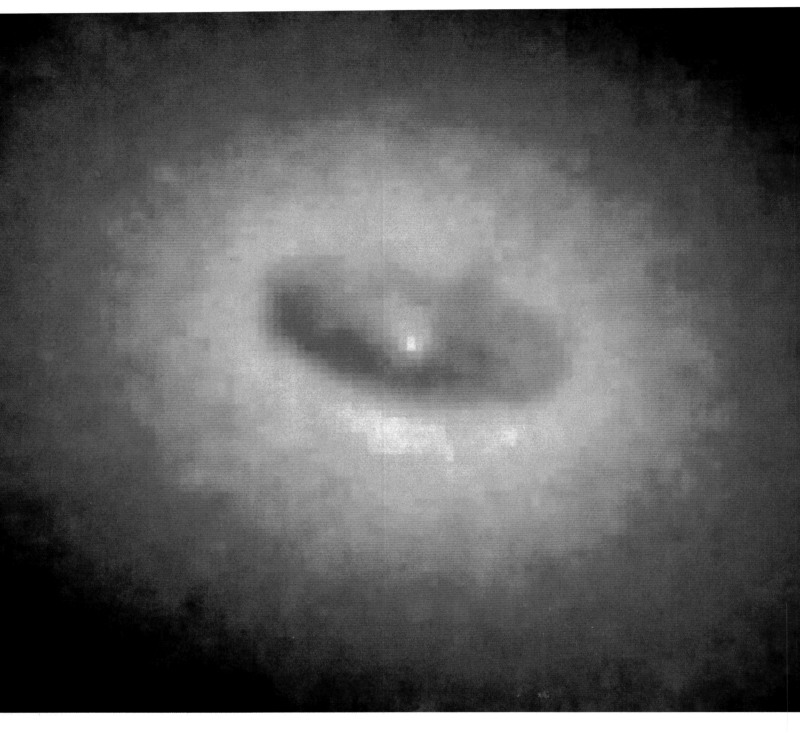

Above: At the heart of the galaxy NGC 4261, a disk of glowing gas circulates around what is thought to be a black hole with a mass ten million times that of our sun.

Opposite: Microwave maps from the COBE satellite may give clues to the Big Bang.

Arno Penzias and Robert Wilson, stumbled across such evidence in the form of a faint hiss of radio noise pervading the Universe. This, the so-called cosmic background radiation, is interpreted as being heat from the Big Bang fireball, emitted at a temperature of thousands of degrees but chilled by the subsequent expansion of the Universe to 454° F (−270° C) today. Such a frigid temperature may scarcely deserve to be termed "heat", but what is remarkable is that empty space should have any measur-

able temperature at all, and the Big Bang seems to be the only plausible explanation. For their astounding discovery, second in importance only to Hubble's recognition that the Universe is expanding, Penzias and Wilson were awarded the Nobel prize.

A further development came in 1992 when a satellite called the Cosmic Background Explorer (COBE) detected tiny 'ripples' in this background warmth, amounting to temperature differences of a

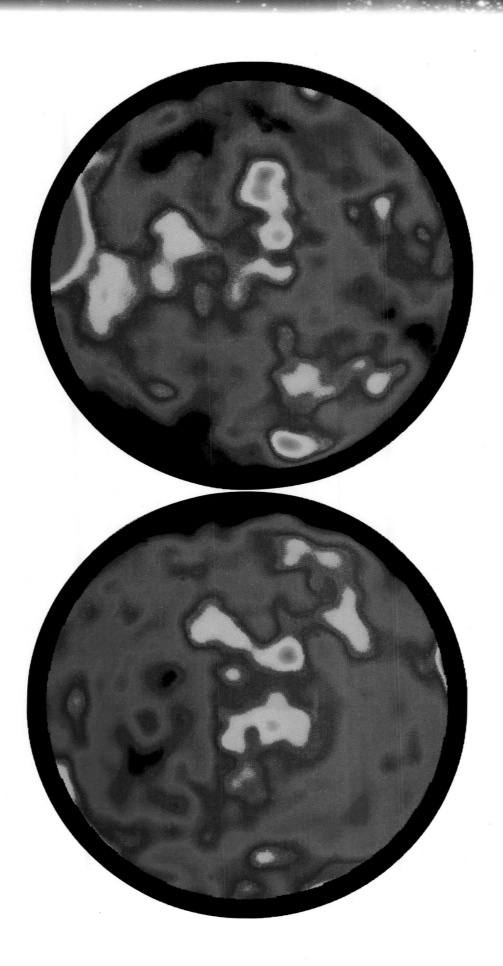

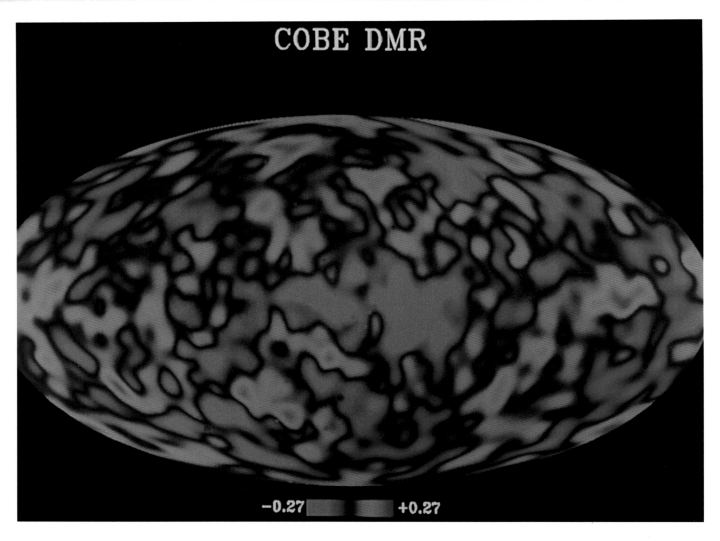

COBE DMR

−0.27   +0.27

Above: Microwave maps taken by the COBE satellite. This false colour image captures the fluctuations of the heat left over from the big bang. Perhaps these fluctuations hold the key to events just before the big bang?

Opposite: Omega Centauri, the brightest globular star cluster. It is located in the southern constellation Centaurus. It has a magnitude of 3.7 and is visible to the unaided eye as a faint luminous patch. Omega Centauri is about 17,000 light-years from Earth and is thus one of the nearer globular clusters. It is estimated to contain hundreds of thousands of stars.

mere 30 millionths of a degree. Such temperature variations mark out denser areas of gas from the Big Bang fireball. They are the oldest structures in the Universe, the foundations on which galaxies and clusters of galaxies were built.

DATING THE CREATION

Since Hubble's day astronomers have sought to answer the most fundamental question of all: when did the Big Bang occur? To find out, we must measure the rate at which the Universe is expanding, a figure known as Hubble's constant. That requires knowing the speed of galaxies and their distance. Speeds are easy enough to measure from the redshift in the galaxies' light, but the difficulty comes with the distances.

Thanks to improvements in distance-measuring techniques, aided by observations from the Hubble Space Telescope, we now have an accurate estimate of Hubble's constant. Put simply, two points separated

by a million light years will be moving apart at a speed of 41,000 miles per hour (66,000 km/h), assuming there is no large mass nearby to disturb them. Two objects twice as far apart are separating at twice the speed, and so on.

Turning this rate of expansion around we find that the galaxies would have taken about 16 billion years to reach their present separations, over three times the age of the Earth (which dates back 4.6 billion years). If the expansion was somewhat faster in the past, as we might expect, then the time taken is reduced by a few billion years, but is still at least twice the age of the Earth and similar to the age of the oldest stars in our Galaxy.

Hence we can say that the Universe was created in the Big Bang about 13 billion years ago, give or take a couple of billion years. Our Galaxy, like most galaxies, began to form soon afterwards, while the Sun and Earth appeared relatively late on the scene.

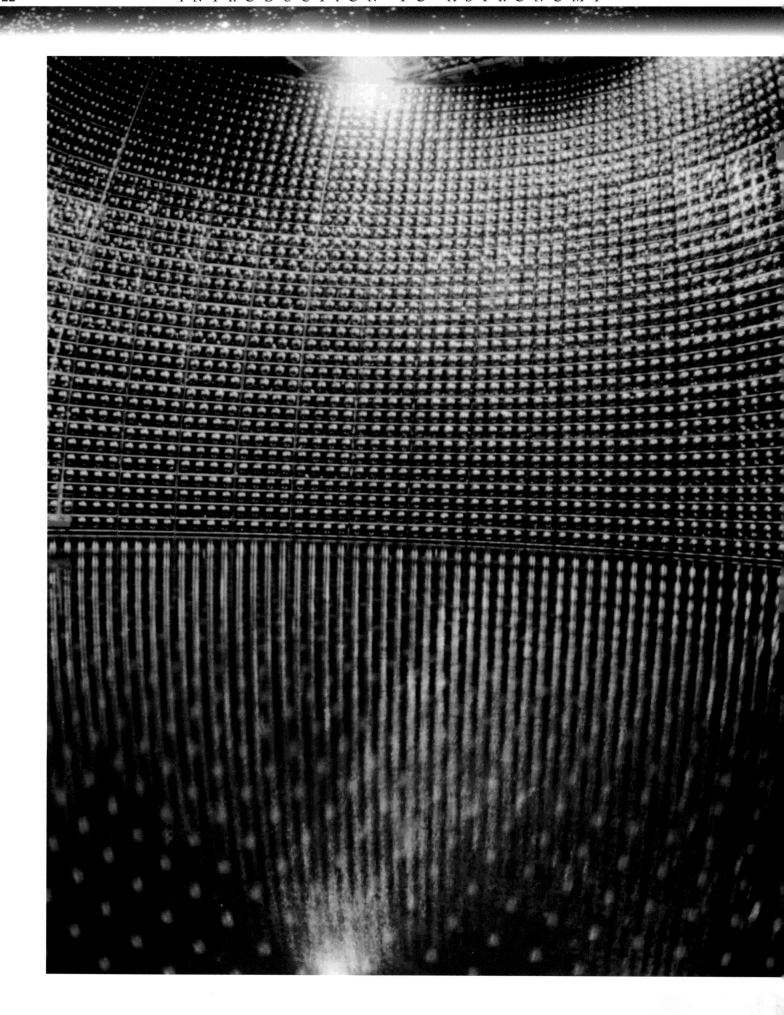

DARK SIDE OF THE UNIVERSE

Will the tide of the expanding Universe ever turn? It depends on the density of matter spread throughout it, but that density is difficult to determine because the Universe contains a great deal more than meets the eye.

For more than half a century, astronomers have lived with an uncomfortable fact: most of the matter in the Universe cannot be seen. Despite its invisibility, this so-called dark matter can be detected from its gravitational effect on the rotation rates of galaxies and on the motions of galaxies in clusters. Galaxies, including our own, possess halos of dark matter.

Some of this matter is probably in the form of objects that are not so much dark as dim – very small stars which shine only feebly. Other options are the remains of stars that have burnt out and collapsed in on themselves creating neutron stars or black holes.

Another form of dark matter – and perhaps the most important of all – may be the subatomic particles called neutrinos, which fill the Universe but are almost undetectable. Neutrinos were long thought to be as weightless as ghosts, but recent experiments have shown that this may not be true after all. Even if a neutrino has only a minute fraction the weight of an electron, there are so many of them – many millions in a volume of space the size of a shoe box – they could outweigh the visible stars and galaxies many times over.

Were the density of the Universe greater than a certain critical value, gravity would brake the expansion of the Universe and eventually throw it into reverse. Tens of billions of years hence, all matter, and space, would rush back together like an incoming tide onto the shores of a Big Crunch.

But, unless there is even more dark matter than astronomers think, the density of the Universe is less than that critical value. Hence there is nothing to stop the Universe from expanding forever. As time runs on into an infinite future, galaxies will become ever more isolated and stars will burn out one by one. Eventually the Universe, its brilliant youth long behind it, will fade out into an eternal, frozen night.

Left: The interior of the Super Kamiokande detector, Japan. This detector consists of 50,000 tonnes of water housed in a container 11 storeys high. It is designed to detect neutrinos, particles that are suspected to be responsible for dark matter. The detector has to be this size as neutrinos interact very weakly with matter. The bulbs on the side of the detector are photomultiplier tubes which are sensitive enough to see a single photon of light. The neutrinos are dectected as they sometimes emit light when they pass through the water.

Overleaf left: The Keck telescopes open for observation. Notice the composite structure of the mirrors. The mirrors of these telescopes are actually many hexagonal pieces that are held together. This is because a single mirror of the same size would sag under its own weight and give imperfect readings.

Overleaf right: The Very Large Array (VLA). These radio dishes can be moved to tailor individual measurements.

BIG EYES...

Telescopes larger than the world has ever before seen are springing up in the clear, dark skies on high mountain tops. Chief among this new breed of optical giants are the twin Keck reflectors atop Mauna Kea, Hawaii, each with a mirror 10 metres (394 inches) wide. These mirrors are not made of a solid piece of glass but consist of 36 hexagonal segments, computer-controlled to focus light from celestial objects into one crisp image.

Two eyes are better than one, so by building telescopes in pairs, such as the Keck instruments, astronomers can increase their ability to distinguish fine detail in remote objects. This same principle is used by the Large Binocular Telescope on Mount Graham, Arizona, which has twin mirrors of 8.4 metres (330 inches) aperture on the same mounting.

Most ambitious of all multi-telescope groupings is the European Southern Observatory's Very Large Telescope, consisting of four 8.2-m (323-inch) reflectors on Cerro Paranal, Chile, which can work singly or in unison, giving the performance of a mirror up to 16 metres in diameter.

Large individual telescopes include the 8.3-m (327-inch) Japanese Subaru reflector on Mauna Kea, and the two identical 8.1-m (320-inch) Gemini Telescopes, one of which studies the northern sky from Mauna Kea and the other the southern sky from Cerro Pachón, Chile. These new eyes on the sky dwarf the venerable but still-active 200-inch (5-m) reflector on Palomar Mountain, California, opened in 1948.

Right: The exterior of one of the Keck Telescopes. The large bay doors shield the interior (seen opposite) of the telescope during bad weather.

...AND EARS

Radio telescopes work like optical reflectors, using a large dish to collect and focus radio waves that are emitted naturally by objects in space. Radio waves have much longer wavelengths than light, so radio telescopes must be correspondingly larger to see as much detail as optical telescopes. Large size makes them difficult to steer – in fact the world's largest radio astronomy dish, 1000 feet (305 metres) in diameter, cannot be steered at all. It lies suspended in a natural hollow between hills near Arecibo, Puerto Rico, scanning the sky overhead as the Earth rotates. The largest fully steerable radio telescope, the Green Bank Telescope at the National Radio Astronomy Observatory in West Virginia, has an elliptical reflector measuring 100 by 110 metres (328 x 360 ft).

Smaller radio dishes are often ganged together, and their output combined to synthesise the view that would be obtained by one very large dish. A prime example is the Very Large Array near Socorro, New Mexico, where 27 movable dishes of 25 metres (82 ft) aperture are arranged in a Y-shape up to 22 miles (36 km) across.

Radio dishes can be spread out much more widely than in the VLA. The 250-ft (76-m) Lovell Telescope at Jodrell Bank, England, is the largest in a network of seven radio telescopes distributed across England, called Merlin, whose ability to see fine detail rivals that of the Hubble Space Telescope. In the widest separations of all, the signals from radio telescopes on different continents are combined to produce, in effect, the performance of a radio telescope as wide as the Earth.

Right: The Very Large Array (VLA).

AN EYE IN SPACE

Opposite: Stars over the Nasa infrared Telescope Facility on Mauna Kea in Hawaii.

Below: This is taken from the Space Shuttle of the launch of the Hubble Space telescope (HST). The HST was one of the largest payloads ever to be carried by the Shuttle.

Launched by the Space Shuttle in 1990, the Hubble Space Telescope (HST) has provided astronomers with a fresh eye on the Universe – but that was not the case at first. Once it was in orbit, astronomers found that the telescope would not focus properly because its mirror had slightly the wrong curvature, a fault not detected by prelaunch tests. In December 1993, astronauts on a repair mission fitted additional optics which sharpened the HST's view.

Although its aperture of 2.4 metres (94 inches) is smaller than the largest telescopes on Earth, the HST can see finer detail and fainter objects because it is above the Earth's atmosphere, which blurs and dims the view of telescopes on the ground. The Hubble Space Telescope is helping to answer questions about the origin and evolution of the Universe that were first posed three quarters of a century ago by the American astronomer Edwin Hubble, in whose honour it is named.

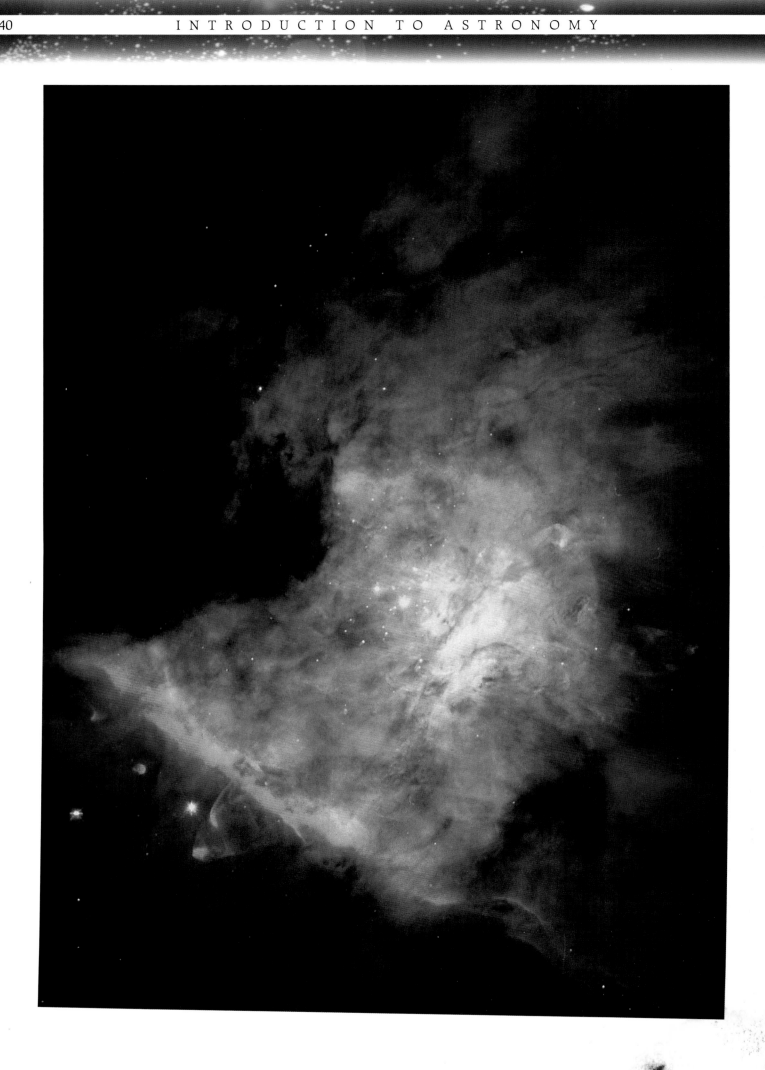

from the dying star forms glowing shells and loops, often of considerable beauty and complexity. The result is termed a planetary nebula, not because it has anything to do with planets but because the rounded disks of the first known examples looked somewhat like planets to old-time observers. Since then many such nebulae have been discovered which are not at all rounded or planet-like in appearance, but the name has stuck.

Stripped bare at the centre of the planetary nebula lies the core of the former red giant, still glowing white-hot but with no more energy being produced within it. Such an object is termed a white dwarf, and their properties are extraordinary. A typical white dwarf is the size of the Earth yet contains about as much matter as the Sun, compressed so densely that a spoonful of it would weigh as much as a truck.

Over billions of years, white dwarfs cool down and fade into obscurity. Should any planets have survived the red giant stage and remain in orbit around our Sun once it has become a white dwarf, they will end up freezing in the darkness.

OUT WITH A BANG

Stars that are many times heavier than the Sun suffer an altogether more cataclysmic demise. When they swell up towards the end of their lives they turn into supergiants, even larger and brighter than red giants. Supergiants are the biggest and brightest of all stars. Examples include Betelgeuse and Rigel, the two brightest stars in Orion, which give out as much light as some 10,000 and 50,000 Suns respectively. Betelgeuse has a diameter at least 500 times that of the Sun, large enough to fill the orbit of the planet Jupiter. A radio message would take well over an hour to cross from one side of such a bloated star to the other.

To power their immense brilliance, supergiants undergo an accelerating succession of nuclear reactions, each requiring higher temperatures than the last. But this spendthrift behaviour exacts a terrible price – the self-destruction of the star. Once the last of the internal energy resources is used up, the star collapses in on itself. This triggers an explosion known as a supernova,

Previous pages left: The Orion Nebula seen through the Hubble Space Telescope. On close inspection it is easy to see the newly formed stars that light up the gasses that make this object so spectacular.

Previous pages right: The Orion Nebula. This beautiful nebula is a fine example of a "stellar nursery" where stars are born. Intense radiation from the new stars cause the surrounding gases to glow. The Orion Nebula is about 1500 light-years from Earth, and about five light-years across.

Left: An image of the Constellation of Orion showing the different colours of the stars. We can use the information of what colour a star is to find out its composition. The constellation is named after the Greek mythological hunter. Orion is one of the most conspicuous constellations and contains many bright stars. One of these, Betelgeuse, is easily distinguished by its reddish colour.

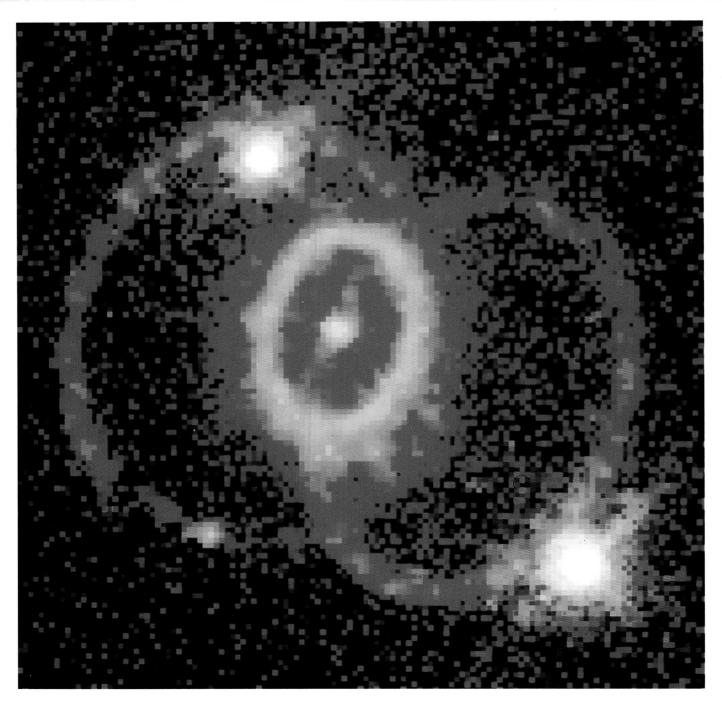

Above: An eerie, nearly mirror-image pair of red luminescent gas "hula-hoops" frame the expanding debris of a star seen as a supernova explosion in 1987.

Opposite: The Southern Cross is visible in this picture of the night sky.

one of the most incredibly violent events in the Universe, which rips the star apart, hurling its outer layers into space at speeds of around 20 million m.p.h. (36 million km/h). For a few weeks, the exploding star blazes as brightly as a billion Suns.

Supernovae in distant galaxies are spotted regularly through telescopes, but only rarely does one occur close enough to us to be visible to the naked eye. A brilliant supernova erupted in the Large Magellanic Cloud in February 1987 and remained visible to the naked eye for most of that year. For some reason, no supernovae have been seen in our Galaxy since 1604 – although one could come at any time.

Supernovae have a relevance to us all, for without them we would not be here. If most of the matter in the Universe is hydrogen and helium, where did the rock and metal of the Earth and other planets come from? Those atoms were forged in the nuclear furnaces of supernovae that erupted before the Sun was born. Scattered into space, they mixed with the existing gas that later gave rise to the Sun and planets, and ultimately life on Earth. We all contain atoms that were created in ancient supernovae.

FAMILY OF THE SUN

Below: The surface of Mercury. Unlike the Earth, Mercury has no atmosphere and so meteors do not burn up on approach to the planet. This is why there are so many craters on the surface.

Opposite: This view of Mercury was sent back from Mariner 10 as the spacecraft sped towards the planet. Eighteen pictures were taken at 42 second intervals to form this photomosaic. The spacecraft was 200 000km from the surface when these images were taken.

We live on planet Earth, a modest-sized member of a family of bodies orbiting the Sun. Collectively, the Sun's family is known as the Solar System. Its full complement is nine planets, their 63 known moons, and countless asteroids and comets.

A general pattern can be discerned among the planets. Those closest to the Sun are small and rocky, while those in the cold outer reaches are large and composed primarily of liquid and gas. On the periphery of the planets is a swarm of icy bodies of which Pluto is the largest.

Gravity imposes a lane discipline on all orbiting objects: the closer in they are, the more quickly they move. Orbital periods range from three months for Mercury, the innermost planet, to nearly 250 years for distant Pluto. Looking from above the Sun's north pole the general pattern of orbital circulation in the Solar System is anticlockwise (i.e. from west to east), although certain moons and comets go against the flow.

MERCURY, CLOSEST TO THE SUN

Innermost of the planets is tiny Mercury, a rocky, airless body only 40% larger than our Moon and strikingly lunar-like in appearance. Photographs of its surface taken in 1974 by NASA's Mariner 10 space probe revealed a heavily cratered landscape, the result of a lifetime of bombardment by meteorites.

Never straying far from the Sun, Mercury is difficult to see from Earth, although at times it can be spotted, huddled low in the evening or morning twilight and glinting like a bright ruddy-hued star. Solar radiation blasts Mercury's surface, sending temperatures on the sun-

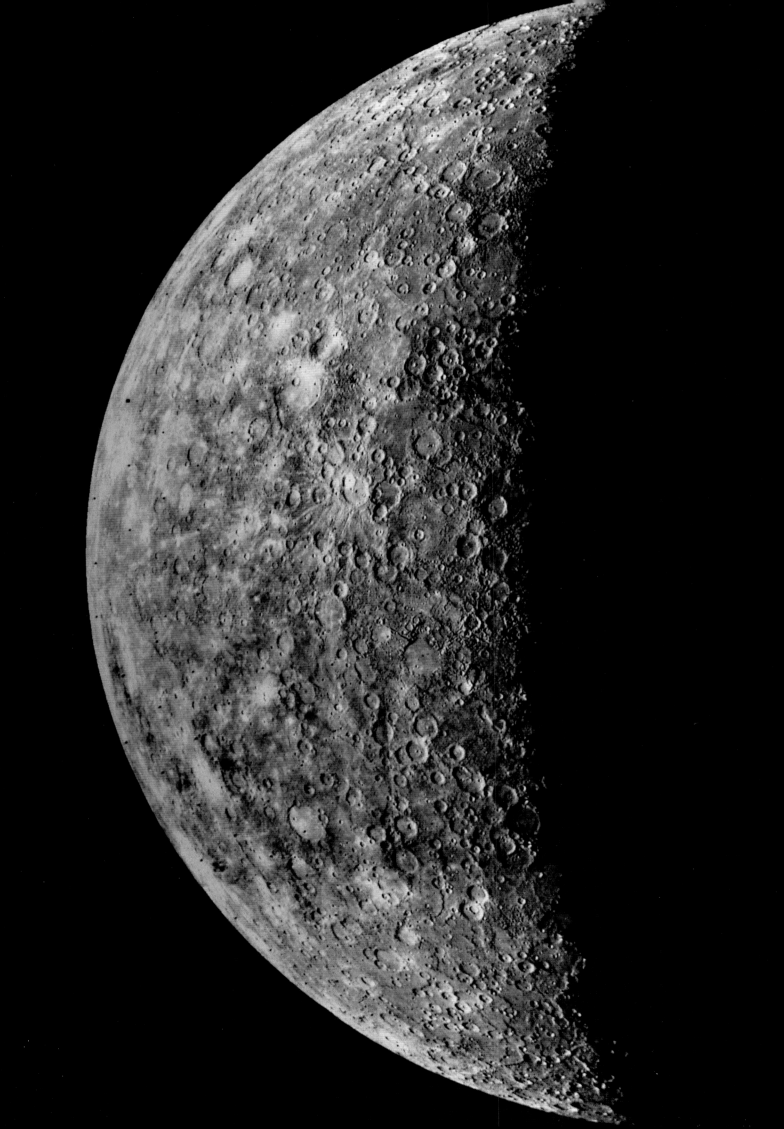

bring a wealth of additional detail into view.

The bright uplands are saturated with craters of all sizes, the scars of meteorites that rained onto the Moon early in its history. By contrast, relatively few craters are to be seen on the dark lowlands, which are deserts of solidified lava that flowed into basins hollowed out by the greatest of the ancient impacts. Unlike the geologically active Earth, the Moon has remained largely unchanged in appearance for most of its life.

American astronauts on the Apollo missions landed on the Moon between 1969 and 1972, bringing samples of it back to Earth for study. One day we may set up permanent bases on the Moon for scientific research, and use it as a staging post to the planets.

MARS, THE RED PLANET

Mars has a special place in human imagining, for it has long been suspected to harbour life. Dark surface markings that changed with the seasons were interpreted as tracts of vegetation, while some imaginative astronomers even claimed to see canals dug by a putative Martian civilisation, inspiring a genre of science fiction stories that included H. G. Wells' War of the Worlds.

Below: Sojourner carried colour cameras and a special spectrometer for geologic and geochemical studies of Martian rocks, soil, and dust.

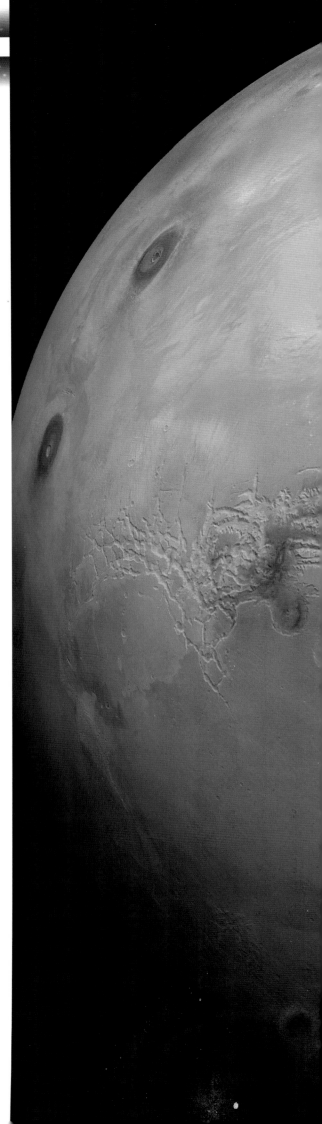

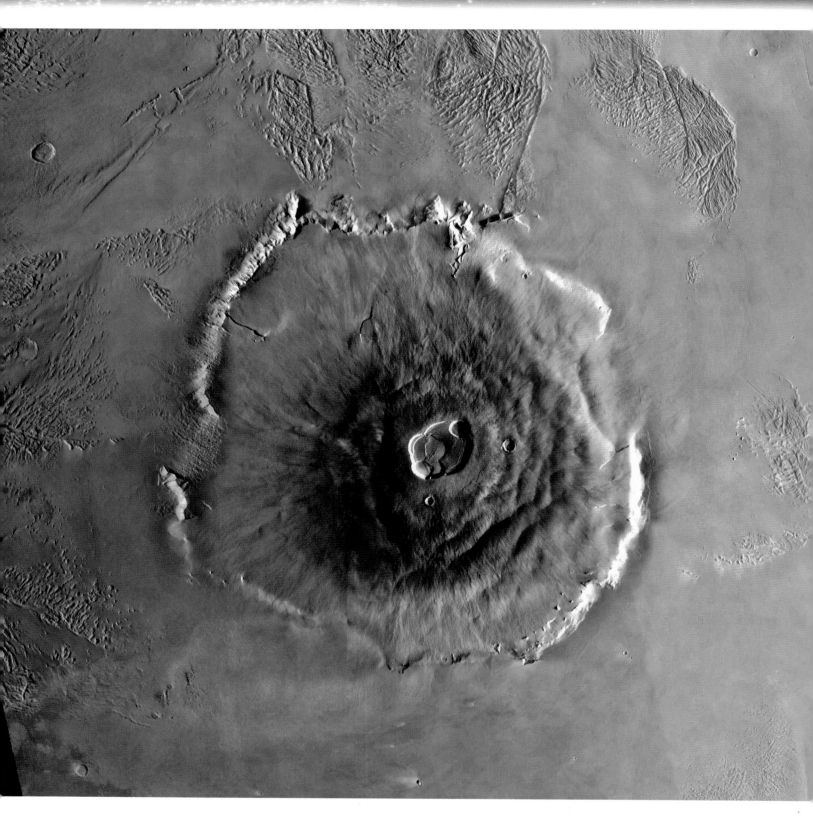

Above: The Olympus Mons is the largest volcano on Mars, about three times the height of Mount Everest and has a diameter of 620km (385 miles).

On the face of it, the speculations were well founded: although only half the size of the Earth, Mars has a day length and seasons similar to ours, an atmosphere with occasional clouds and white polar caps. In reality, space probes have discovered that conditions there are harsher than the old astronomers ever supposed.

Its surface is a rocky, lifeless desert, stained red by iron oxide – common rust – from which Mars takes its popular name, the Red Planet. Yet this desert is not hot – temperatures rarely rise above freezing because the planet's atmosphere is too thin to retain heat.

Parts of the surface look like the Moon,

dotted with giant impact craters, while elsewhere huge volcanoes tower to more than twice the height of Mount Everest. Most disappointingly, the dark markings turned out to be nothing more than areas of darker rock that are alternately covered and uncovered by wind-blown dust, while the canals were simply illusory.

The debate is not yet over, though. There are unmistakable signs of dried-up

Above: This is a picture of the remote controlled crawler Sojourner about to leave the lander Pathfinder that brought it to Mars.

Below left: This electron microscope image is a close-up of the centre of a meteorite that came from Mars. While the exact nature of these tube-like structures is not known, one interpretation is that they may be microscopic fossils of primitive, bacteria-like organisms that may have lived on Mars more than 3.6 billion years ago.

Below: Deimos, the outer of the two satellites of Mars. Both these moons were discovered by the American astronomer Asaph Hall in 1877.

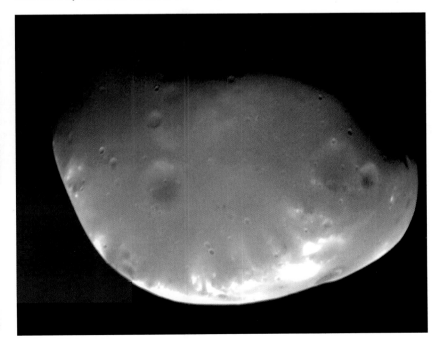

river beds on the surface of Mars, evidence that the planet had a milder, wetter climate in the past. Perhaps simple life once got started on Mars but died out when the climate changed. A group of scientists has reported traces of possible ancient microbial life in a rare type of meteorite thought to have been blasted off the surface of

Opposite: The Great Red Spot on Jupiter. The Great Red Spot was discovered in 1665 by the French astronomer Gian Domenico Cassini with the aid of one of the earliest telescopes, and it has existed at least since that time.

Right top to bottom):
(A) This image mosaic of asteroid 253 Mathilde is constructed from four images acquired by the NEAR spacecraft on June 27, 1997. The images were taken from a distance of 1,500 miles (2,400 kilometres).

(B) A picture of the Asteroid Gaspra as seen by the Galileo probe.

(C) The asteroids Mathilde, Gaspra and Ida pictured together on the same scale to compare sizes.

(D) In 1993-94 the spacecraft Galileo produced images showing an asteroid that has its own tiny moon. The asteroid Ida is orbited at a distance of roughly 100 km by a rock that is about 1.5 km in diameter and is the smallest known natural satellite in the solar system.

Far right: The Great Red Spot on Jupiter as seen by the Galileo probe. As part of its mission Galileo dropped a probe into the atmosphere of Jupiter to analyse the composition of the Jovian atmosphere.

Mars. Their conclusions are controversial, however. When future space probes bring back samples from Mars, we should know for sure.

ASTEROIDS, DEBRIS OF THE SOLAR SYSTEM

Asteroids are chunks of rock and metal left over from the formation of the Solar System. Most of them orbit in a broad

(A)

(B)

(C)

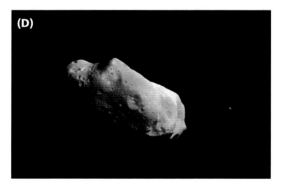
(D)

band, over 100 million miles (170 million km) wide, between Mars and Jupiter, marking the transition from the solid inner planets to the outer gaseous giants. There are estimated to be millions of them, but even if they were all collected together they would form a body far smaller than our own Moon. The largest asteroid is Ceres, about 600 miles (1,000 km) in diameter, but most are no more than a mile or so across.

Some asteroids venture away from the main belt and present an impact hazard if they pass close to the Earth. It is now thought that the dinosaurs, along with many other living things, died out from the effects of an asteroid collision with the Earth 65 million years ago. Smaller fragments of asteroids hit the Earth all the time – these are termed meteorites. In the Arizona desert, Meteor Crater is the result of an impact by an iron meteorite about 50,000 years ago.

JUPITER, THE LARGEST OF ALL

Eleven times the diameter of the Earth and weighing more than twice as much as all the other planets combined, Jupiter is the giant of the Sun's family. It is a world totally unlike the solid inner planets, being

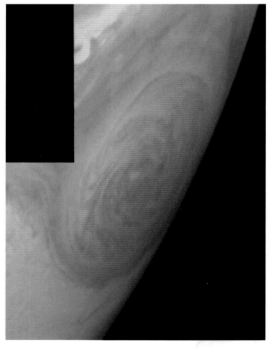

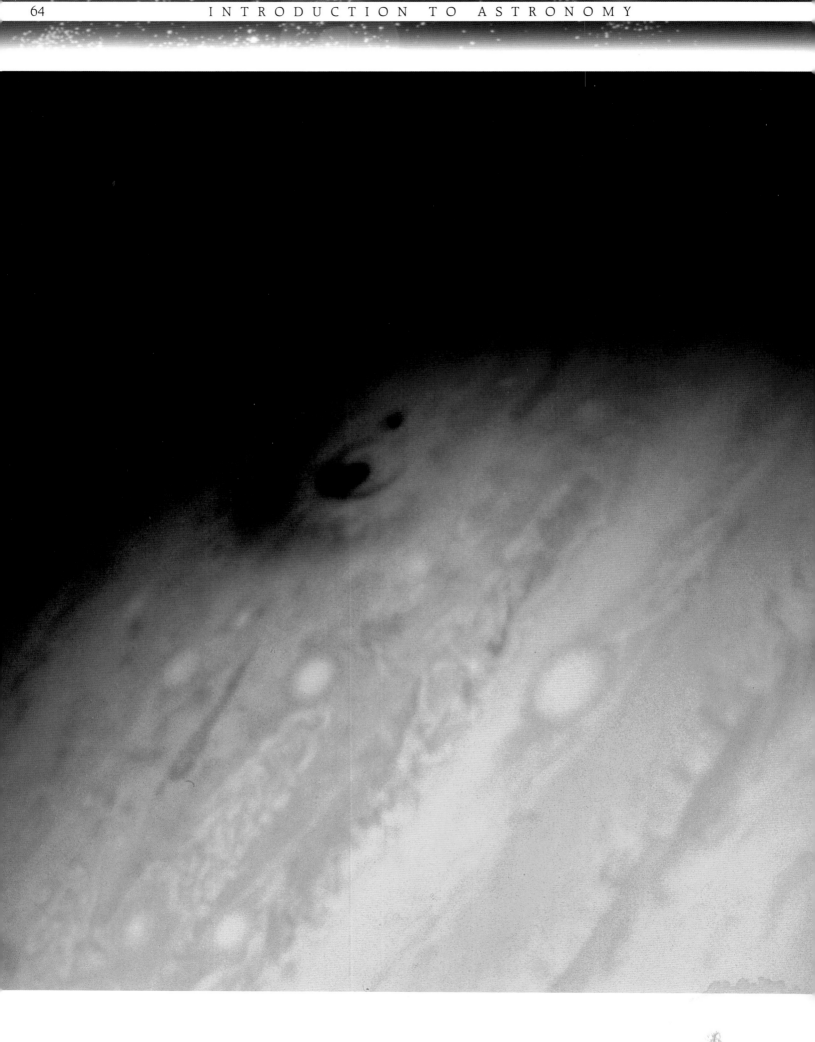

Left: This picture of Hupiter's moon Io, is a composite of images taken by the *Galileo* spacecraft on March 29, 1998. Volcanic activity is rendered as a series of dark spots, while the lighter blues and greens indicate the presence of sulphur dioxide or other sulphur compounds.

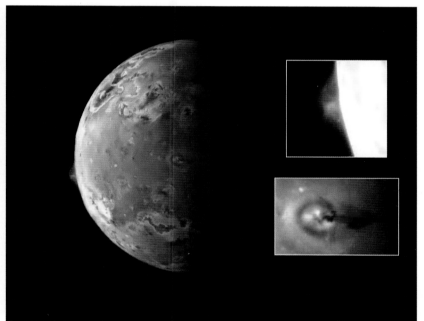

basically a ball of liquid hydrogen and helium topped by a deep layer of clouds.

To the naked eye Jupiter appears as a bright, white star. Through a telescope, we can see the colourful clouds that envelop it. Jupiter's rapid axial spin – once in under ten hours, fastest of all the planets – draws the clouds into parallel bands, a pattern noticeably different from the equator-to-pole circulation in the Earth's atmosphere. Features in the clouds usually persist for only a few weeks, although some white spots have lasted for decades and the Great Red Spot, a swirling storm cloud three times larger than the Earth, has been followed for centuries.

Beneath the clouds there is no solid surface on which we could land. With increasing depth, the planet's immense gravita-

Above: A false-colour composite of the surface of Io, a satellite of Jupiter. Two volcanic plumes are visible. The plume on the limb of the satellite is roughly 140 km (87 miles) high.

Opposite: The impact site of fragment G of the comet Shoemaker-Levy 9 on Jupiter. This was one of the biggest scars on the Jovian atmosphere. The picture was taken one and a quarter hours after the impact itself as the site rotated into view.

Right: Saturn as viewed by the Hubble Space Telescope. The shadow of the planet can be clearly seen on the rings behind the planet.

tional pull compresses hydrogen and helium into liquids, although there may be a solid centre, as unreachable as the iron core of the Earth.

Sixteen moons orbit Jupiter, like a mini solar system. The four largest – Io, Europa, Ganymede and Callisto – are visible through binoculars as pinpoints of light, changing places from night to night as they orbit the planet. These moons are large enough to be considered worlds in their own right, notably Ganymede, 3,270 miles (5,262 km) in diameter, the largest moon in the Solar System and bigger than the planet Mercury. Io, similar in size to our Moon, is punctured by erupting volcanoes, while Europa has a surface of jumbled ice floes that may overlie a deep ocean.

SATURN, THE RINGED PLANET

Nearly ten times farther from the Sun than we are, Saturn was the most distant planet known to ancient astronomers. In many ways it is a smaller version of Jupiter, but the bright rings encircling its equator endow it with a unique beauty.

One curiosity of Saturn is that its average density is less than that of water; so, difficult though it is to imagine, Saturn would float if a sufficiently large ocean existed. With a spin rate second only to that of Jupiter, low-density Saturn bulges more at the waist than any other planet – its equatorial diameter is 10% greater than from pole to pole.

Saturn's defining feature, the rings, consist of an orbiting swarm of rocky and icy chunks, some as large as a house. These orbiting objects arrange themselves into thousands of narrow lanes, giving the rings a grooved appearance like the surface of an old-fashioned gramophone record when seen in close-up. A line of five Earths could be laid across the rings from inner edge to outer, although faint outer extensions, invisible in the photographs here, stretch several times further. The rings may be relatively recent in origin, probably the debris of one or more passing comets that were captured by Saturn within the past few hundred million years.

Overleaf: Saturn from the Hubble Space Telescope in ultraviolet as well as the usual visible light wavelengths. The Hubble Space Telescope allows us to view wavelengths from objects in the sky that would normally be absorbed by the Earth's atmosphere.

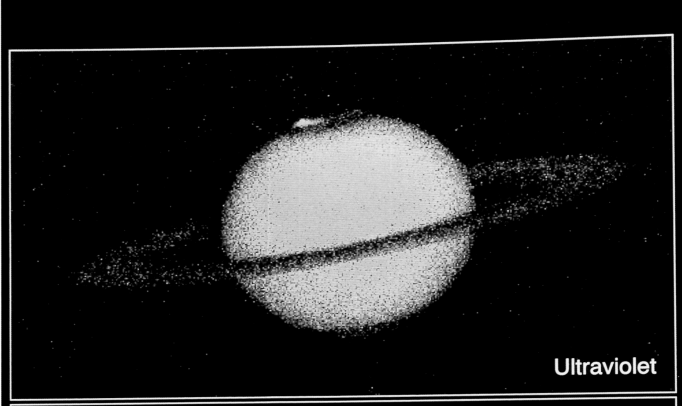

Ultraviolet

Visible

Saturn Aurora
Hubble Space Telescope · WFPC2

Saturn has 18 known moons, more than any other planet, and others may be discovered by a space probe called Cassini that is due to arrive at Saturn in 2004. Most notable of Saturn's family is Titan, the second-largest moon in the Solar System and bigger than the planet Mercury. Titan is the only moon with a substantial atmosphere. The Cassini probe will drop a lander craft called Huygens onto Titan's surface to learn more about conditions there.

Above: Aurorae glowing at the poles of Saturn, seen by the Hubble Space Telescope.

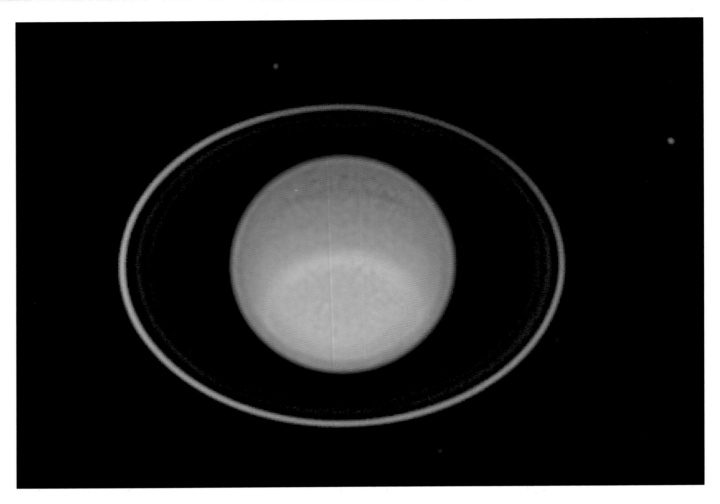

Above: Uranus and its rings from the Hubble Space Telescope , Wide Field Planetary Camera 2. Uranus is the seventh planet in order of distance from the Sun. Its low density (1.285 grams per cubic centimetre) and large size (radius four times that of the Earth) place it among the four giant planets, all of which are without solid surfaces.

Opposite: A picture of Neptune taken by Voyager 2 showing the "Great Dark Spot". This large oval cloud feature, about the same size as Earth, was discovered by Voyager 2 in 1989 but seemed to have vanished five years later.

URANUS, THE TILTED PLANET

Uranus was discovered by chance one night in March 1781 by an amateur astronomer named William Herschel while he was scanning the sky with a home-made telescope from his back garden in the English country town of Bath. This new planet, never previously seen on account of its faintness, turned out to lie twice as far from the Sun as Saturn, and its discovery thereby doubled the size of the known Solar System.

Four times larger than the Earth, Uranus is one of the giant, gaseous planets but has the blandest surface of them all. Its near-featureless clouds are tinged a distinctive green by the presence of methane gas in the overlying atmosphere.

Long ago, probably while it was forming, Uranus suffered a blow that knocked it nearly horizontal, so that its axis of rotation lies in almost the same plane as its orbit. At times its poles can point directly towards the Sun, giving rise to extreme seasons.

Uranus has a system of faint and narrow rings, discovered in 1977. Because of the planet's extreme tilt they seem to lie almost upright, giving Uranus a bullseye appearance. As well as the rings, Uranus has 17 known moons, two of them spotted as recently as 1997.

NEPTUNE, THE OUTERMOST GIANT

Neptune's existence was predicted before it was actually discovered when astronomers noticed that Uranus was not keeping to its predicted orbit, as though being pulled off course by the gravitational tug of some yet-unseen planet. Two mathematicians – John Couch Adams in England and Urbain Le Verrier in France – independently began calculations to locate such a planet, and came to similar conclusions. While the English search stalled, Le Verrier sent his prediction to Berlin

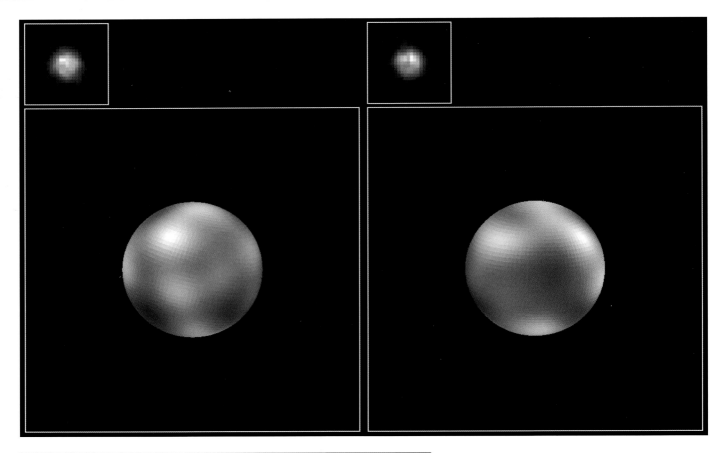

Above: Pluto and Charon imaged by the Hubble Space Telescope.

Top: Images of the surface of Pluto taken by the Hubble Space Telescope faint object camera. Bright and dark markings on its surface are thought to be caused by patches of frost. In close up it would probably look like Neptune's largest moon, Triton.

Observatory, where Johann Galle found the new planet on the night of September 23, 1846.

Similar in size, Neptune and Uranus appeared at first to be as alike as two peas in a pod (although Neptune is bluish rather than pea-green because it has more methane gas above its clouds). Neptune, however, is warmer inside, which stirs up the atmosphere to create cloud features that are largely missing on Uranus.

Neptune has eight known moons, the largest of which, Triton, orbits from east to west, the opposite direction to the general traffic flow in the Solar System. Triton is actually bigger than the planet Pluto.

Probably it was once a separate body like Pluto but was captured into orbit around Neptune.

PLUTO, THE DISTANT DWARF

Pluto, the outermost planet, was discovered in 1930 by Clyde Tombaugh as the result of a deliberate photographic search for new planets at Lowell Observatory in Arizona. As well as being the most distant planet, Pluto is also the smallest, only two-thirds the size of our Moon. In many ways it is a misfit, having the most elliptical and highly tilted orbit of all the planets. In fact for part of its orbit it is closer to the Sun than Neptune, as it was between February 1977 and February 1999.

Pluto has one moon, Charon, fully half its size, and the two are often regarded as a double planet. Charon orbits Pluto every 6.4 days, the same time that the planet takes to spin on its axis, and therefore hangs permanently above one point on Pluto, like a geostationary communications satellite over the Earth. NASA, the American space agency, is considering a mission called the Pluto–Kuiper Express to fly past Pluto and Charon in 2012, and then on into the Kuiper Belt – the domain of the comets.

COMETS, WANDERERS BETWEEN THE PLANETS

Comets are icy bodies that loop around the Sun on highly elongated orbits, becoming visible to us for a few weeks, or occasionally months, before they recede back into the darkness. A comet can grow to an enormous size, but its only solid part is the nucleus, a dirty snowball of frozen gas and dust usually no more than a few miles across. Approaching the Sun, the nucleus warms up and releases fountains of gas and dust to create a glowing halo, the coma, many times larger than the Earth but far thinner than the air we breathe. In large comets, gas and dust streams away to form a diaphanous tail, which in cases such as the magnificent comet Hale–Bopp of 1997 can stretch farther than the distance from the Earth to the Sun.

Comets originate at the edge of the Solar System, where their nuclei are preserved in deep-freeze. Those with orbital periods of less than a century or two are thought to come from a region just beyond the orbit of Pluto called the Kuiper Belt. Comets with the longest orbital periods (thousands of years or more) dive in towards the Sun from a more distant halo around the Solar System known as the Oort Cloud, extending halfway to the nearest star, where they swarm in their unseen billions. Comets are named after their discoverers, so find a comet and your name will ride for ever in the sky.

Dust particles shed by comets streak into the Earth's atmosphere, burning up by friction to produce a flash of light popularly called a shooting star, but which astronomers term a meteor. A handful of such encounters can be seen on any clear night, but several times a year the Earth enters an interplanetary dust storm when it passes close to a comet's orbit, and we see a shower of meteors such as the bright Perseids of August.

Overleaf: In early 1997 Comet Hale-Bopp put on a spectacular naked-eye celestial display for people everywhere. Here the comet is seen over Stonehenge.

OTHER SOLAR SYSTEMS

Our Solar System is thought to have formed about 4.6 billion years ago from a ring of gas and dust left in orbit around our infant Sun. Astronomers are now finding signs of planet-building in progress elsewhere, most graphically around a star 63 light years away in the southern hemisphere named Beta Pictoris.

Even more excitingly, in recent years full-grown planets have been detected around other stars. Planets of other stars are too faint to see directly, but their presence can be inferred from the slight wobble of their parent star as the planet orbits it. So far the techniques are only sensitive enough to detect the wobbles caused by planets the size of Jupiter or larger, but smaller, Earthlike planets may also exist unnoticed.

Some estimates suggest that as many as one star in every ten may have planets. If planets are common throughout the Galaxy, then there is a good chance that other life exists out there as well.

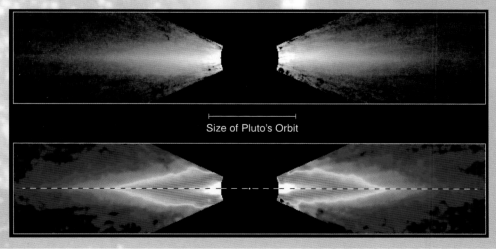

Size of Pluto's Orbit

Left: This Hubble Space Telescope image of the star Beta Pictoris reveals a 200-billion mile diameter dust disk encircling the star. This disk shows an unexpected warp. Researchers say the warp can be best explained as caused by the gravitational pull of an unseen planet roughly the size of Jupiter.

SHADOW PLAY

All planets and their moons cast shadows, which stretch unnoticed into space. Occasionally, though, the Sun, Earth and Moon line up so that the Earth's shadow falls on the Moon or that of the Moon falls on the Earth, causing an eclipse.

 As seen from any one place on Earth, eclipses of the Moon are more common than solar ones, although less spectacular. Over a period of an hour or more, the Moon moves into the Earth's shadow until it is finally engulfed. Even when fully eclipsed, the Moon can remain faintly visible. Some light diffuses through the Earth's atmosphere and into the shadow, softly illuminating the Moon with a reddish glow.

Solar eclipses occur when the Moon crosses in front of the Sun, blotting out some or all of its light. Partial solar eclipse can go unnoticed, since the sky does not darken appreciably even when half the Sun is covered, but total eclipses are among the finest spectacles in nature. Astronomers travel around the world to see the few precious minutes of totality, when the sky goes dark in daytime and the Sun's corona, a normally invisible halo of gas, comes into view.

Left 1–7: As the Moon orbits the Earth every month, we see its familiar sequence of phases. Yet the surface features visible remain the same, because the same side of it is always facing us, a result of billions of years of gravitational interaction between Earth and Moon.

Opposite: When the Moon moves through the shadow of the Earth it loses its bright direct illumination by the Sun, although its disk still remains faintly visible. As the shadow of the Earth is directed away from the Sun, a lunar eclipse can occur only at the time of Full Moon – that is, when the Moon is on the side of the Earth opposite to that of the Sun.

PLANETARY DATA

Mercury

Diameter:	3,032 miles (4,880 km)
Average distance from Sun:	36.0 million miles (57.9 million km)
Time to orbit Sun:	87.97 days
Time to spin on axis:	58.65 days
Tilt of axis:	0°
Number of moons:	0
Surface temperature:	800°F to -280°F (427°C to -173°C)

Venus

Diameter:	7,521 miles (12,104 km)
Average distance from Sun:	67.2 million miles (108.2 million km)
Time to orbit Sun:	224.7 days
Time to spin on axis:	243 days
Tilt of axis:	177.4°
Number of moons:	0
Surface temperature:	867°F (464°C)

Earth

Diameter at equator:	7,926 miles (12,756 km)
Average distance from Sun:	93.0 million miles (149.6 million km)
Time to orbit Sun:	365.26 days
Time to spin on axis:	23.93 hours
Tilt of axis:	23.4°
Number of moons:	1
Surface temperature (average):	59°F (15°C)

The Moon

Diameter at equator:	2,160 miles (3,476 km)
Average distance from Earth:	238,900 miles (384,400 km)
Time to orbit Earth:	27.32 days
Time to spin on axis:	27.32 days
Surface temperature:	253°F to -387°F (123°C to -233°C)

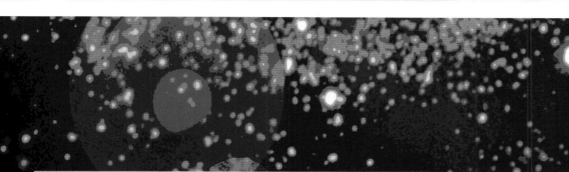

Mars

Diameter at equator:	4,222 miles (6,794 km)
Average distance from Sun:	141.6 million miles (227.9 million km)
Time to orbit Sun:	686.98 days
Time to spin on axis:	24.62 hours
Tilt of axis:	25.2°
Number of moons:	2
Surface temperature (average):	-81°F (-63°C)

Jupiter

Diameter at equator:	88,846 miles (142,984 km)
Average distance from Sun:	483.7 million miles (778.4 million km)
Time to orbit Sun:	11.86 years
Time to spin on axis:	9h 51m (equator)
Tilt of axis:	3.1°
Number of moons:	16
Surface temperature: -	163°F (-108°C)

Saturn

Diameter at equator:	74,897 miles (120,536 km)
Average distance from Sun:	886.5 million miles (1,426.7 million km)
Time to orbit Sun:	29.45 years
Time to spin on axis:	10h 14m (equator)
Tilt of axis:	26.7°
Number of moons:	18
Surface temperature:	-218°F (-139°C)

Uranus

Diameter at equator:	31,763 miles (51,118 km)
Average distance from Sun:	1,784.0 million miles (2,871.0 million km)
Time to orbit Sun:	84.02 years
Time to spin on axis:	17h 14m
Tilt of axis:	97.9°
Number of moons:	17 plus
Surface temperature:	-323°F (-197°C)

Neptune

Diameter at equator:	30,775 miles (49,528 km)
Average distance from Sun:	2,795.1 million miles (4,498.3 million km)
Time to orbit Sun:	164.79 years
Time to spin on axis:	16h 7m
Tilt of axis:	28.3°
Number of moons:	8
Surface temperature:	-330°F (-201°C)

Pluto

Diameter at equator:	1,430 miles (2,302 km)
Average distance from Sun:	3,670.1 million miles (5,906.4 million km)
Time to orbit Sun:	247.92 years
Time to spin on axis:	6.39 days
Tilt of axis:	122.5°
Number of moons:	1
Surface temperature:	-370°F (-223°C)

INDEX